TRANSLATIONS FROM THE PHILOSOPHICAL WRITINGS OF GOTTLOB FREGE

Translations from the Philosophical Writings of Gottlob Frege

EDITED BY

PETER GEACH

Professor of Logic, University of Leeds

AND

MAX BLACK

Professor of Philosophy, Cornell University

BASIL BLACKWELL

OXFORD

1977

© in this translation, Basil Blackwell 1952

First Edition 1952
Second Edition 1960
Reprinted 1966, 1969, 1977
ISBN 0 631 05810 0

PRINTED IN GREAT BRITAIN
FOR BASIL BLACKWELL & MOTT LTD.
BY THE CAMELOT PRESS LIMITED, SOUTHAMPTON
AND BOUND BY
THE KEMP HALL BINDERY, OXFORD

PREFACE

ONE aim of this volume is to make available to English readers Frege's more important logical essays, which have long been buried in various German periodicals (mostly now defunct). Besides these we have given certain extracts from his *Grundgesetze der Arithmetik*; these can be understood in the light of the essays, without the reader's needing to follow the chain of deduction in the *Grundgesetze*.

Special attention should be paid to Frege's discussion of Russell's paradox in the appendix to Vol. ii of the *Grundgesetze*. It is discreditable that logical works should repeat the legend of Frege's abandoning his researches in despair when faced with the paradox; in fact he indicates a line of solution, which others might well have followed out farther.

The authorship of the various versions is stated in the table of contents. All versions have been revised with a view to uniform rendering of Frege's special terms; a glossary of these terms is supplied.

Footnote flags such as [A],[B], relate to translators' footnotes; other footnotes are Frege's own.

Acknowledgments are due to the editors of *Mind* and the *Philosophical Review*, for permission to use versions first published there. Acknowledgment is also due for use of the translations made from Vol. i of the *Grundgesetze* by P. E. B. Jourdain and J. Stachelroth (which were first published in the *Monist*, 1915–17), to the owners of the copyright, whom it has unfortunately proved impossible to trace. Professor Ryle and Lord Russell have been most helpful by lending works of Frege that were otherwise almost unobtainable.

MAX BLACK.
P. T. GEACH.

NOTE TO SECOND EDITION

WE have made a number of corrections for this second impression. Mr. Michael Dummett was kind enough to check the whole translation and give us his advice. A new footnote on p. 243 refers to recent work on 'Frege's Way Out'.

M. B.
P. T. G.

CONTENTS

GLOSSARY

The special terms used by Frege have been rendered as follows:

Anschauung	intuition, experience
Art des Gegebenseins	mode of presentation
bedeuten[1]	stand for
Bedeutung[1]	reference [occasionally: what . . . stands for]
Begriff	concept [in the logical sense]
Behauptungssatz	declarative sentence
beurtheilbarer Inhalt	possible content of judgment
eigentliche Zahl	actual number [as opposed to a *numeral*]
Figur[2]	figure
formal	formal(ist)
Gebild[2]	character, structure
Gedanke[3]	thought
Gegenstand	object
gewöhnliche (Bedeutung)	customary (reference)
gleich, Gleichheit[4]	equal, equality
inhaltlich	meaningful [an epithet of arithmetic interpreted in a nonformalist fashion]
objektiv[5]	objective
Rechenspiel	calculating game [arithmetic on the formalist view]
Rechnungsart	arithmetical operation [addition, subtraction, etc.]
Satz	sentence, proposition, theorem, clause [according to context]

[1] The natural rendering of these words would be 'mean' and 'meaning'; this rendering is actually required for their occurrence in German works quoted by Frege, and for his own use of the words when alluding to such quotations. But 'meaning' in ordinary English often answers to Frege's *Sinn* rather than *Bedeutung*. Russell's 'indicate' and 'indication' are barred because we need 'indicate' rather for *andeuten*. The renderings given here seem to be the simplest means of expressing Frege's thought faithfully. Philosophical technicalities, like 'referent' or 'denotation' or 'nominatum,' would give a misleading impression of Frege's style.

[2] These two words are used to refer to supposedly meaningless marks, such as numerals are on the formalist theory. Both words must often also be rendered '(chess) piece.'

[3] Frege regards a 'thought' as sharable by many thinkers, and thus as objective.

[4] Frege remarks concerning these words that *he* takes them to express strict identity, but other mathematicians disagree; 'equality' therefore seems preferable to 'identity.'

[5] It must be carefully noticed that the German words rendered 'object' and 'objective' are not connected in etymology or in Frege's mind. Concepts are fundamentally different from *objects*; but they are *objective*, i.e. not private to a particular thinker.

Sinn	sense
Stufe	level [of a concept or function]
(unbestimmt) andeuten[1]	indicate (indefinitely)
ungerade (Bedeutung)	indirect (reference) [i.e. pertaining to words in *oratio obliqua* or virtual *oratio obliqua*]
ungesättigt[2]	'unsaturated'
Vorstellung[3]	idea, image [regarded as essentially private]
Wahrheitswerth	truth-value
Werthverlauf	value-range, range of values [of a function]

[1] This term is applied to pronouns (e.g. relative pronouns) and also to letters used as variables. (Frege disliked the term 'variable'; cf. his essay *What is a Function?*)

[2] This is Frege's term for such fragmentary expressions as '—— conquered Gaul' or 'the capital of ——'; and also for their *Bedeutung*, i.e. what they stand for. He may well have had in mind unsaturated molecules, which, without dissolution of their existing structure, can take up more atoms. To emphasize, as Frege does, the metaphorical nature of the term, we always write it in quotation marks.

[3] Contrasted with *Begriff* and *Gedanke* (q.v.).

BEGRIFFSSCHRIFT
a formalized Language of pure Thought modelled upon the Language of Arithmetic

First published in 1879

I. EXPLANATION OF THE SYMBOLS

§ 1

THE symbols used in the general theory of magnitude fall into two kinds. The first consists of the letters; each letter represents either an indeterminate number or an indeterminate function. This indeterminateness makes it possible to express by means of letters the general validity of propositions; e.g.: $(a + b)c = ac + bc$. The other kind contains such symbols as $+$, $-$, $\sqrt{}$, 0, 1, 2; each of these has its own proper meaning.[A]

I adopt this fundamental idea of distinguishing two kinds of symbols (which unfortunately is not strictly carried out in the theory of magnitude[*]) *in order to make it generally applicable in the wider domain of pure thought.* Accordingly, I divide all the symbols I use into *those that can be taken to mean various things* and *those that have a fully determinate sense.* The first kind are *letters,* and their main task is to be the expression of *generality.* For all their indeterminateness, it must be laid down that a letter *retains* in a given context the meaning once given to it.

§ 2. *Judgment*

A judgment is always to be expressed by means of the sign

$$\vdash$$

This stands to the left of the sign or complex of signs in which the content of the judgment is given. If we *omit* the little vertical
p. 2] stroke at the left end of the horizontal stroke, then the

---

[*] Consider the symbols l, log, sin, Lim.

[A] I render *Bedeutung* by 'meaning' or 'significance' throughout this work, since Frege had not yet begun to use it in his own special sense. Various other words, e.g. *Begriff* ('concept') and *Vorstellung* ('idea') are also used in a less precise sense than he later gave to them.

1

judgment is to be transformed into *a mere complex of ideas*; the author is not expressing his recognition or non-recognition of the truth of this. Thus, let

$$\vdash\!\!-\!A^*$$

mean the judgment: 'unlike magnetic poles attract one another.' In that case

$$-\!\!\!-\!A$$

will not express this judgment; it will be intended just to produce in the reader the idea of the mutual attraction of unlike magnetic poles—so that, e.g., he may make inferences from this thought and test its correctness on the basis of these. In this case we *qualify* the expression with the words *'the circumstance that'* or *'the proposition that.'*

Not every content can be turned into a judgment by prefixing $\vdash\!\!-$ to a symbol for the content; e.g. the idea 'house' cannot. Hence we distinguish contents that *are*, and contents that *are not*, *possible contents of judgment.*†

As a constituent of the sign $\vdash\!\!-$ *the horizontal stroke combines the symbols following it into a whole; assertion, which is expressed by the vertical stroke at the left end of the horizontal one, relates to the whole thus formed.* The horizontal stroke I wish to call the *content-stroke*, and the vertical the *judgment-stroke*. The content-stroke is also to serve the purpose of relating any sign whatsoever to the whole formed by the symbols following the stroke. *The content of what follows the content-stroke must always be a possible content of judgment.*

§ 3

A distinction of *subject* and *predicate* finds *no place* in my way of representing a judgment. In order to justify this, let me observe that there are two ways in which the content of two judgments may differ; it may, or it may not, be the case that all inferences that can be drawn from the first judgment when combined with

* I use Greek uncials as abbreviations; if I give no special explanation of them I wish the reader to supply an appropriate sense.

† On the other hand, the circumstance of there being houses (or *a* house) is a possible content of judgment. (Cf. § 12.) But the idea 'house' is only part of this. In the proposition 'Priam's house was of wood' we cannot replace 'house' by 'circumstance of there being a house.' . . .

p. 3] certain other ones can always also be drawn from the second when combined with the same other judgments. The two propositions 'the Greeks defeated the Persians at Plataea' and 'the Persians were defeated by the Greeks at Plataea' differ in the former way; even if a slight difference of sense is discernible, the agreement in sense is preponderant. Now I call the part of the content that is the same in both the *conceptual content*. *Only this* has significance for our symbolic language; we need therefore make no distinction between propositions that have the same conceptual content. When people say 'the subject is the concept with which the judgment is concerned,' this applies equally well to the object. Thus all that can be said is: 'the subject is the concept with which the judgment is chiefly concerned.' In language the place occupied by the subject in the word-order has the significance of a *specially important* place; it is where we put what we want the hearer to attend to specially. (Cf. also § 9.) This may, e.g., have the purpose of indicating a relation between this judgment and others, and thus making it easier for the hearer to grasp the whole sequence of thought. All such aspects of language are merely results of the reciprocal action of speaker and hearer; e.g. the speaker takes account of what the hearer expects, and tries to set him upon the right track before actually uttering the judgment. In my formalized language there is nothing that corresponds; only that part of judgments which affects the *possible inferences* is taken into consideration. Whatever is needed for a valid inference is fully expressed; what is not needed is for the most part not indicated either; *no scope is left for conjecture.* In this I follow absolutely the example of the formalized language of mathematics; here too, subject and predicate can be distinguished only by doing violence to the thought. We may imagine a language in which the proposition 'Archimedes perished at the capture of Syracuse' would be expressed in the following way: 'the violent death of Archimedes at the capture of Syracuse is a fact.' You may if you like distinguish subject and predicate even here; but the subject contains the whole p. 4] content, and the only purpose of the predicate is to present this in the form of a judgment. *Such a language would have only a single predicate for all judgments, viz. 'is a fact.'* We see that there is no question here of subject and predicate in the ordinary sense.

Our symbolic language is a language of this sort; the symbol $\vdash$——
is the common predicate of all judgments.

In my first draft of a formalized language I was misled by the example of ordinary language into compounding judgments out of subject and predicate. But I soon convinced myself that this was obstructive of my special purpose and merely led to useless prolixity.

§ 4

The following remarks are to explain the significance, relative to our purpose, of the distinctions people make as regards judgments.

People distinguish *universal* and *particular* judgments; this is properly a distinction between contents, not between judgments. *What one ought to say is: 'a judgment whose content is universal (particular).'* For the content has these properties even when it is presented, *not* as a judgment, but as a proposition. (Cf. § 2.)

The same thing holds good for negation. Thus, in an indirect proof one says 'suppose the segments AB and CD were not equal.' There is a negation involved here in the content: the segments AB and CD not being equal; but this content, though suitable matter for judgment, is not presented in the shape of a judgment. Negation thus attaches to the content, no matter whether this occurs in the shape of a judgment or not. I therefore hold it more suitable to regard negation as a mark of a *possible content of judgment.*

The distinction of judgments into categorical, hypothetical, and disjunctive seems to me to have a merely grammatical significance.*

What distinguishes the apodeictic from the assertoric judgment is that it indicates the existence of general judgments from which the proposition may be inferred—an indication that is absent in the assertoric judgment. If I term a proposition 'necessary,' then I am giving a hint as to my grounds for judgment. *But this does*
p. 5] *not affect the conceptual content of the judgment; and therefore the apodeictic form of a judgment has not for our purposes any significance.*

If a proposition is presented as possible, then either the speaker is refraining from judgment, and indicating at the same time that

* My grounds for this will be brought out by the whole of this work.

he is not acquainted with any laws from which the negation of the proposition would follow; or else he is saying that the negation of the proposition is in general false. In the latter case we have what is usually termed a *particular affirmative judgment.* (Cf. § 12.) 'It is possible that the Earth will one day collide with another celestial body' is an example of the first case; 'a chill may result in death,' of the second case.

§ 5. *Conditionality*

If A and B stand for possible contents of judgment (§ 2), we have the four following possibilities:

(i) A affirmed, B affirmed;
(ii) A affirmed, B denied;
(iii) A denied, B affirmed;
(iv) A denied, B denied.

$$\vdash\!\!\!\begin{array}{c} A \\ B \end{array}$$

stands for the judgment that *the third possibility is not realized, but one of the other three is.* Accordingly, the denial of

$$\begin{array}{c} A \\ B \end{array}$$

is an assertion that the third possibility is realized, i.e. that A is denied and B affirmed.

From among the cases where

$$\begin{array}{c} A \\ B \end{array}$$

is affirmed, the following may be specially emphasized:

(1) A *is to be affirmed.*—In this case the content of B is quite indifferent. Thus, let A mean: $3 \times 7 = 21$; let B stand for the circumstance of the sun's shining. Here only the first two cases out of the four mentioned above are possible. A causal p. 6] connexion need not exist between the two contents.

(2) B *is to be denied.*—In this case the content of A is indifferent. E.g. let B stand for the circumstance of perpetual motion's being possible, and A for the circumstance of the world's

being infinite. Here only the second and fourth of the four cases are possible. A causal connexion between A and B need not exist.

(3) One may form the judgment

$$\vdash\!\!\!\begin{array}{c} A \\ B \end{array}$$

without knowing whether A and B are to be affirmed or denied. E.g. let B stand for the circumstance of the Moon's being in quadrature with the Sun, and A the circumstance of her appearing semicircular. In this case we may render

$$\vdash\!\!\!\begin{array}{c} A \\ B, \end{array}$$

by means of the conjunction 'if'; 'if the Moon is in quadrature with the Sun, then she appears semicircular.' The causal connexion implicit in the word 'if' is, however, not expressed by our symbolism; although a judgment of this sort can be made only on the ground of such a connexion. For this connexion is something general, and as yet we have no expression for generality. (Cf. § 12.)

The vertical stroke joining the two horizontal ones is to be called the *conditional stroke*. The part of the upper horizontal stroke that occurs to the left of the conditional stroke is the content-stroke relative to the meaning of the complex symbol

$$\begin{array}{c} A \\ B, \end{array}$$

which has just been defined; any symbol that is meant to relate to the content of the expression as a whole will be attached to this content-stroke. The part of the horizontal stroke lying between A and the conditional stroke is the content-stroke of A. The horizontal stroke to the left of B is the content-stroke of B. . . .

p. 7]   § 6

From the explanation given in § 5 it is obvious that from the two judgments

$$\vdash\!\!\!\begin{array}{c} A \\ B \end{array} \quad \text{and} \quad \vdash\!\!\!-- B$$

there follows the new judgment $\vdash\!\!-\!\!- A$. Of the four cases enumerated above, the third is excluded by

$$\vdash\!\!\begin{array}{l} \!-\!\!\!\!-A \\ \!\!\!\!-B \end{array}$$

and the second and fourth by: $\vdash\!\!-\!\!- B$,

so that only the first remains. . . .

    p. 9] Following Aristotle, logicians enumerate a whole series of kinds of inference; I use just this one—at any rate in all cases where a new judgment is derived from more than one single judgment. For the truth implicit in another form of inference can be expressed in a judgment of the form: if M holds and N holds then $\varLambda$ holds also; symbolically,

From this judgment, and $\vdash\!\!-\!\!- N$, and $\vdash\!\!-\!\!- M$, $\vdash\!\!-\!\!- \varLambda$ will then follow as above. An inference, of whatever kind, may be reduced to our case in this way. Accordingly it is possible to get along with a single form of inference; and therefore perspicuity demands that we should do so. Moreover, if we did not there would be no reason to confine ourselves to the Aristotelian forms of inference; we could go on adding new forms indefinitely. . . . *This restriction to a single form of inference is however in no way meant to express a psychological proposition; we are just settling a question of formulation, with a view to the greatest convenience for our purpose. . . .*

p. 10]   § 7. *Negation*

    If a small vertical stroke is attached to the lower side of the content-stroke, this shall express the circumstance of the content's not being the case. Thus, e.g., the meaning of

$$\vdash_{\top}\!\!- A$$

is: 'A is not the case.' I call this small vertical stroke the *negation-stroke.* The part of the horizontal stroke occurring to the right of the negation-stroke is the content-stroke of A; the part occurring to the left of the negation-stroke is the content-stroke of the negation of A. Here as elsewhere in our symbolism, no judgment is performed if the judgment-stroke is absent.

$$\bar{\top}\, A$$

merely requires the formation of the idea that A is not the case, without expressing whether this idea is true.

We now deal with some cases where the symbols of conditionality and negation are combined.

$$\vdash_{\displaystyle \top}\!\begin{array}{l} A \\ B \end{array}$$

means: 'the case in which B is to be affirmed and the negation of A is to be denied does not occur'; in other words, 'the possibility of affirming both A and B does not exist,' or 'A and B are mutually exclusive.' Thus only the three following cases remain:

A affirmed, B denied;
A denied, B affirmed;
A denied, B denied.

From what has already been said, it is easy to determine the meaning possessed by each of the three parts of the horizontal stroke preceding A.

$$\vdash_{\displaystyle \bot}\!\begin{array}{l} A \\ B \end{array}$$

means: 'the case in which A is denied and the negation of B is p. 11] affirmed does not exist'; or, 'A and B cannot both be denied.' There remains only the following possibilities:

A affirmed, B affirmed;
A affirmed, B denied;
A denied, B affirmed.

A and B between them exhaust all possibilities. Now the words 'or,' 'either—or,' are used in two ways. In its first meaning,

$$\text{`}A \text{ or } B\text{'}$$

means just the same as

$$\top\!\begin{array}{l} A \\ B, \end{array}$$

i.e. that nothing besides A and B is thinkable. E.g. if a gaseous mass is heated, then either its volume or its pressure increases. Secondly, the expression

$$\text{`}A \text{ or } B\text{'}$$

may combine the meaning of

$$\vdash\!\!\!\!\top\!\!\!\begin{array}{l}\;A\\ \llcorner\; B\end{array} \quad\text{and that of}\quad \vdash\!\!\!\!\top\!\!\!\begin{array}{l}\;A\\ \llcorner_{\top}\; B\end{array}$$

so that (i) there is no third possibility besides A and B, (ii) A and B are mutually exclusive. In that case only the following two possibilities remain out of the four:

　A affirmed, B denied;
　A denied, B affirmed.

Of these two uses of the expression 'A or B' the more important is the first, which does not exclude the coexistence of A and B; *and we shall use the word 'or' with this meaning.* Perhaps it is suitable to distinguish between 'or' and 'either—or,' regarding only the latter as having the subsidiary meaning of mutual exclusion. In that case

$$\top\!\!\!\!-\!\!\!\begin{array}{l}\;A\\ \llcorner_{\top}\; B\end{array}$$

may be rendered by 'A or B' . . .

p. 12]

$$\vdash\!\!-\!\!\top\!\!\!\!\top\!\!\!\begin{array}{l}\;A\\ \llcorner\; B\end{array}$$

means:

$$\text{`}\top\!\!\!\!\top\!\!\!'\!\!\!\begin{array}{l}\;A\\ \llcorner\; B\end{array}$$

is denied'; or 'the case in which A and B are both affirmed occurs.' Contrariwise, the three possibilities left open by

$$\top\!\!\!\!\top\!\!\!\begin{array}{l}\;A\\ \llcorner\; B\end{array}$$

are excluded. Accordingly, we may render

$$\vdash\!\!-\!\!\top\!\!\!\!\top\!\!\!\begin{array}{l}\;A\\ \llcorner\; B\end{array}$$

by 'both A and B are facts.' . . .

We have here expressed 'and' by means of the symbols for conditionality and negation; instead, we might conversely express conditionality by means of a symbol for 'and' and the symbol for negation. We might, say, introduce

$$\left\{ \begin{array}{l} \Gamma \\ \Delta \end{array} \right.$$

as a symbol for the combined content of Γ and Δ, and then render

p. 13]

$$\underset{}{\top}\!\!\!\underset{L}{}\begin{array}{l} A \\ B \end{array}$$

by

$$\top\left\{ \begin{array}{l} \top A \\ B \end{array} \right.$$

I chose the other way because inference seemed to be expressed more simply that way. The distinction between 'and' and 'but' is of such a kind as not to be expressed in our symbolism. The speaker uses 'but' when he wants to hint that what follows is different from what you might at first suppose.

$$\vdash\!\!\top\underset{\top}{\overline{}}\begin{array}{l} B \\ A \end{array}$$

means: 'the case where A and B are both denied occurs.' We may thus render it as:

'neither A nor B is a fact.'

Clearly we are here concerned with the words 'or,' 'and,' 'neither . . . nor' only in so far as they combine possible contents of *judgment*.

§ 8. *Equality of content*

Equality of content differs from conditionality and negation by relating to names, not to contents. Elsewhere, signs are mere proxies for their content, and thus any phrase they occur in just expresses a relation between their various contents; but names at once appear *in propria persona* so soon as they are joined
p. 14] together by the symbol for equality of content; for this signifies the circumstance of two names' having the same content. Thus, along with the introduction of a symbol for equality

of content, all symbols are necessarily given a double meaning—the same symbols stand now for their own content, now for themselves. At first sight this makes it appear as though it were here a matter of something pertaining only to *expression*, not to *thought*; as though we had no need of two symbols for the same content, and therefore no need of a symbol for equality of content either. In order to show the unreality of this appearance, I choose the following example from geometry. Let a fixed point A lie on the circumference of a circle, and let a straight line rotate around this. When this straight line forms a diameter, let us call the opposite end to A the point B corresponding to this position. Then let us go on to call the point of intersection of the straight line and the circumference, the point B

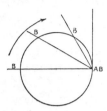

As the line turns in the direction of the arrow, B moves towards A, till they coincide.

corresponding to the position of the straight line at any given time; this point is given by the rule that to continuous changes in the position of the straight line there must always correspond continuous changes in the position of B.[B] Thus the name B has an indeterminate meaning until the corresponding position of the straight line is given. We may now ask: What point corresponds to the position of the straight line in which it is perpendicular to the diameter? The answer will be: The point A. The name B thus has in this case the same content as the name A; and yet we could not antecedently use just one name, for only the answer to the question justified our doing so. The same point is determined in a double way:

(1) It is directly given in experience;

(2) It is given as the point B corresponding to the straight line's being perpendicular to the diameter.

To each of these two ways of determining it there answers a separate name. The need of a symbol for equality of content thus rests on the following fact: The same content can be fully determined in different ways; and *that*, in a particular case, *the same* content actually is given by *two ways of determining it*, is the content of a *judgment*. Before this judgment is made, we must supply, corresponding to the two ways of determination,

[B] We have added a diagram to help the reader.

two different names for the thing thus determined. The judgment p. 15] needs to be expressed by means of a symbol for equality of content, joining the two names together. It is clear from this that different names for the same content are not always just a trivial matter of formulation; if they go along with different ways of determining the content, they are relevant to the essential nature of the case. In these circumstances the judgment as to equality of content is, in Kant's sense, synthetic. A more superficial reason for introducing a symbol for equality of content is that sometimes it is convenient to introduce an abbreviation in place of a lengthy expression; we then have to express equality of content between the abbreviation and the original formula.

$$\vdash (A \equiv B)$$

is to mean: *the symbol A and the symbol B have the same conceptual content, so that A can always be replaced by B and conversely.*

§ 9. *The Function*

Let us suppose that there is expressed in our formalized language the circumstance of hydrogen's being lighter than carbon dioxide. In place of the symbol for hydrogen we may insert the symbol for oxygen or nitrogen. This changes the sense in such a way that 'oxygen' or 'nitrogen' enters into the relations that 'hydrogen' stood in before. If an expression is thought of as variable in this way, it is split up into a constant part representing the totality of these relations and a symbol, imagined as replaceable by others, that stands for the object related by the relations. I call the one part a function, the other an argument. This distinction has nothing to do with the conceptual content; it concerns only our way of looking at it. In the manner of treatment just indicated, 'hydrogen' was the argument and 'being lighter than carbon dioxide' the function; but we can equally look at the same conceptual content in such a way that 'carbon dioxide' is the argument and 'being heavier than hydrogen' is the function. p. 16] We need in this case merely to imagine 'carbon dioxide' as replaceable by other ideas like 'hydrochloric acid gas' or 'ammonia'.

'The circumstance of carbon dioxide's being heavier than

hydrogen' and 'The circumstance of carbon dioxide's being heavier than oxygen' are the same function with different arguments if we treat 'hydrogen' and 'oxygen' as arguments; on the other hand, they are different functions of the same argument if we regard 'carbon dioxide' as the argument.

Let our example now be: 'the circumstance that the centre of mass of the solar system has no acceleration provided that none but internal forces act on the solar system.' Here 'solar system' occurs in two places. We may therefore regard this as a function of the argument 'solar system' in various ways, according as we imagine 'solar system' to be replaceable at its first occurrence or at its second or at both (in the last case, replaceable by the same thing both times). These three functions are all different. The proposition 'Cato killed Cato' shows the same thing. If we imagine 'Cato' as replaceable at its first occurrence, then 'killing Cato' is the function; if we imagine 'Cato' as replaceable at its second occurrence, then 'being killed by Cato' is the function; finally, if we imagine 'Cato' as replaceable at both occurrences, then 'killing oneself' is the function.

The matter may now be expressed generally as follows:

Suppose that a simple or complex symbol occurs in one or more places in an expression (whose content need not be a possible content of judgment). If we imagine this symbol as replaceable by another (the same one each time) at one or more of its occurrences, then the part of the expression that shows itself invariant under such replacement is called the function; and the replaceable part, the argument of the function.

By this definition, something may occur in the function both as an argument and also at positions where it is not regarded as replaceable; we must thus distinguish argument–positions in the function from other positions.

p. 17] I should like at this point to give a warning against a fallacy that ordinary language easily leads to. Comparing the two propositions

'the number 20 can be represented as the sum of four squares'

and

'every positive integer can be represented as the sum of four squares,' it seems possible to regard 'being representable as the sum of four squares' as a function whose argument is 'the number 20' one time and 'every positive integer' the other time. We may see that this view is mistaken if we observe that 'the number 20' and 'every positive integer' are not concepts of the same rank. What is asserted of the number 20 cannot be asserted in the same sense of [the concept] 'every positive integer'; of course it may in certain circumstances be assertible of every positive integer. The expression 'every positive integer' just by itself, unlike 'the number 20,' gives no complete idea; it gets a sense only through the context of the sentence.

We attach no importance to the various ways that the same conceptual content may be regarded as a function of this or that argument, so long as function and argument are completely determinate. But if the argument becomes *indeterminate*, as in the judgment: 'whatever arbitrary positive integer you may take as argument for "being representable as the sum of four squares," the proposition always remains true,' then the distinction between function and argument becomes significant as regards the *content*. Conversely, the argument may be determinate and the function indeterminate. In both cases, in view of the contrast *determinate—indeterminate* or *more and less determinate*, the whole proposition splits up into *function* and *argument* as regards its own content, not just as regards our way of looking at it.

Suppose that a symbol occurring in a function has so far been imagined as not replaceable; if we now imagine it as replaceable at some or all of the positions where it occurs, * *this way of looking at it* p. 18] *gives us a function with a further argument besides the previous one.* In this way we get *functions of two or more arguments.* E.g. 'the circumstance of hydrogen's being lighter than carbon dioxide' may be regarded as a function of the arguments 'hydrogen' and 'carbon dioxide.'

The speaker usually intends the subject to be taken as the principal argument; the next in importance often appears as the object. Language has the liberty of arbitrarily presenting one or

---

* Or again: if a symbol already regarded as replaceable is now imagined to be replaceable at those of its occurrences which were previously regarded as constant.

another part of the proposition as the principal argument by a choice between inflexions and words, e.g. between

active and passive,
'heavier' and 'lighter,'
'give' and 'receive';

but this liberty is restricted by lack of words.

§ 10

In order to express an indeterminate function of the argument A, we put A in brackets after a letter, as in

$$\Phi(A)$$

Similarly

$$\Psi(A,B)$$

means a function (not further determined) of the two arguments A and B. Here the places of A and B within the brackets represent the places occupied by A and B in the function (whether A and B each occupy one place in it or more). Accordingly in general

$$\Psi(A,B) \text{ and } \Psi(B,A)$$

are different.

Indeterminate functions of several arguments are expressed similarly.

$$\vdash\!\!-\!\Phi(A)$$

may be read as '*A* has the property Φ'.

$$\vdash\!\!-\!\Psi(A,B)$$

may be read as '*B* stands in the Ψ-relation to *A*' or as '*B* is a result of applying the operation Ψ to the object *A*.'

In the expression

$$\Phi(A)$$

p. 19] the symbol Φ occurs in one place; and we may imagine it replaced by other symbols Ψ, X, so as to express different functions of the argument *A*; *we may thus regard $\Phi(A)$ as a function of the argument Φ*. This makes it specially clear that the concept of function in Analysis, which in general I have followed, is far more restricted than the one developed here.

§ 11. *Generality*

In the expression for a judgment, the complex symbol to the right of ⊢── may always be regarded as a function of one of the symbols that occur in it. *Let us replace this argument with a Gothic letter, and insert a concavity in the content-stroke, and make this same Gothic letter stand over the concavity*: e.g.:

$$\vdash\overset{a}{\smile}\!\!-\!\varPhi(a)$$

This signifies the judgment that the function is a fact whatever we take its argument to be. A letter used as a functional symbol, like $\varPhi$ in $\varPhi(A)$, may itself be regarded as the argument of a function; accordingly, it may be replaced by a Gothic letter, used in the sense I have just specified. The only restrictions imposed on the meaning of a Gothic letter are the obvious ones: (i) that the complex of symbols following a content-stroke must still remain a possible content of judgment (§ 2); (ii) that if the Gothic letter occurs as a functional symbol, account must be taken of this circumstance. *All further conditions imposed upon the allowable substitutions for a Gothic letter must be made part of the judgment.* From such a judgment, therefore, we can always deduce any number we like of *judgments with less general content*, by substituting something different each time for the Gothic letter; when this is done, the concavity in the content-stroke vanishes again. The horizontal stroke that occurs to the left of the concavity in

$$\vdash\overset{a}{\smile}\!\!-\!\varPhi(a)$$

is the content-stroke for [the proposition] that $\varPhi(a)$ holds good whatever is substituted for a; the stroke occurring to the right of p. 20] the concavity is the content-stroke of $\varPhi(a)$—we must here imagine something definite substituted for a.

By what was said before about the meaning of the judgment-stroke, it is easy to see what an expression like

$$-\overset{a}{\smile}\!\!-\!X(a)$$

means. This expression may occur as part of a judgment, as in

$$\vdash\!\!\!\overset{a}{\smile}\!\!-X(a),\qquad \vdash\!\!\begin{array}{l} \rule{2cm}{0.4pt}\ A \\ \underline{\quad\overset{a}{\smile}\!\!-X(a)} \end{array}$$

It is obvious that from these judgments we cannot infer less general judgments by substituting something definite for **a**, as we can from

$$\vdash\overset{a}{\smile}\!\!-X(a)$$

$\vdash\!\!\!\overset{a}{\smile}\!\!-X(a)$ serves to deny that $X(a)$ is always a fact whatever we substitute for **a**. But this does not in any way deny the possibility of giving **a** some meaning $\varDelta$ such that $X(\varDelta)$ is a fact.

$$\vdash\!\!\begin{array}{l} \rule{2cm}{0.4pt}\ A \\ \underline{\quad\overset{a}{\smile}\!\!-X(a)} \end{array}$$

means that the case in which $-\overset{a}{\smile}\!\!-X(a)$ is affirmed and A denied does not occur. But this does not in any way deny the occurrence of the case in which $X(\varDelta)$ is affirmed and A denied; for, as we have just seen, $X(\varDelta)$ may be affirmed and nevertheless $-\overset{a}{\smile}\!\!-X(a)$ denied. Thus here likewise we cannot make an arbitrary substitution for **a** without prejudice to the truth of the judgment. This explains why we need the concavity with the Gothic letter written on it; *it delimits the scope of the generality signified by the letter. A Gothic letter retains a fixed meaning only within its scope*; the same Gothic letter may occur within various scopes in the same judgment, and the meaning we may ascribe to it in one scope does not extend to any other scope. The scope of one Gothic letter may include that of another, as is shown in p. 21]

$$\vdash\overset{a}{\smile}\!\!\begin{array}{l} \rule{2cm}{0.4pt}\ A(a) \\ \underline{\quad\overset{e}{\smile}\!\!-\ B(a,\,e)} \end{array}$$

In this case *different* letters must be chosen; we could not replace **e** by **a**. It is naturally legitimate to replace a Gothic letter everywhere in its scope by some other definite letter, provided that there are still different letters standing where different letters stood before. This has no effect on the content. *Other substitutions are permissible only if the concavity directly follows the judgment stroke*, so that the scope of the Gothic letter is constituted by the content of the whole judgment. Since this is a specially important case, I shall introduce the following abbreviation: *an italic letter is always to have as its scope the content of the whole judgment*, and this scope is not marked out by a concavity in the content stroke. If an italic letter occurs in an expression not preceded by a judgment stroke, the expression is senseless. *An italic letter may always be replaced by a Gothic letter that does not yet occur in the judgment*; in this case the concavity must be inserted immediately after the judgment-stroke. E.g. for

$$\vdash\!\!-\!\!X(a)$$

we may put

$$\vdash\!\!\underset{}{\cup}^{a}\!\!-\!\!X(a)$$

since *a* occurs only in the argument-position within $X(a)$.

Likewise it is obvious that from

$$\vdash\!\!\!\begin{array}{c}\rule{0.4em}{0pt}\Phi(a)\\ \rule{0.4em}{0pt}A\end{array}$$

we may deduce

$$\vdash\!\!\!\begin{array}{c}\overset{a}{\cup}\!\!-\!\!\Phi(a)\\ \rule{0.4em}{0pt}A\end{array}$$

if A is an expression in which a does not occur, and a occupies only argument-positions in $\Phi(a)$. If $-\underset{}{\cup}^{a}\!\!-\!\!\Phi(a)$ is denied, we must be able to specify a meaning for *a* such that $\Phi(a)$ is denied. Thus if $-\underset{}{\cup}^{a}\!\!-\!\!\Phi(a)$ were denied and *A* affirmed, we should have to be able to specify a meaning for *a* such that *A* was affirmed and $\Phi(a)$ denied. But since we have

p. 22]

$$\vdash\!\!\!\begin{array}{c}\rule{0.4em}{0pt}\Phi(a)\\ \rule{0.4em}{0pt}A\end{array}$$

we cannot do so; for this formula means that whatever *a* may be the case in which $\Phi(a)$ would be denied and *A* affirmed does not occur. Hence we likewise cannot both deny $-\smile^a-\Phi(a)$ and affirm A: i.e.

$$\vdash \begin{array}{c} \smile^a-\Phi(a) \\ \hline\ -A \end{array}$$

. . . Similarly when we have several conditional strokes.

§ 12

We now consider certain combinations of symbols.

p. 23].
$$\vdash\vdash\smile^a-X(a)$$

means that we can find something, say $\varDelta$, such that $X(\varDelta)$ is denied. We may thus render it as: 'there are some things that have not the property X.'
The sense of

$$\vdash\smile^a\dashv X(a)$$

is different. This means: 'Whatever a may be, $X(a)$ must always be denied,' or 'there is not something with the property X,' or (calling something that has the property X, a X) 'there is no X.'

$$-\smile^a\dashv\varLambda(a) \text{ is denied by}$$

$$\vdash\vdash\smile^a\dashv\varLambda(a).$$

This may thus be rendered as 'there are $\varLambda$'s.'*

$$\vdash\smile^a\begin{array}{c} \ulcorner P(a) \\ \llcorner X(a) \end{array}$$

means: 'whatever may be substituted for a, the case in which $P(a)$ would have to be denied and $X(a)$ affirmed does not occur.' It is thus possible that, for some possible meanings of a,

$P(a)$ must be affirmed and $X(a)$ affirmed; for others,
$P(a)$ must be affirmed and $X(a)$ denied; for others again,
$P(a)$ must be denied and $X(a)$ denied.

---

* This must be understood as including the case 'there is a $\varLambda$.' E.g. if $\varLambda(x)$ stands for the circumstance that x is a house, then

$$\vdash\vdash\smile^a\dashv \varLambda(a)$$

means 'there are houses or at least one house.' Cf. § 2, footnote †.

We can thus give the rendering: 'If something has the property X, then it has also the property P,' or 'every X is a P,' or 'all X's are P's.'

This is the way causal connexions are expressed.

$$\vdash \overset{a}{\smile} \sqsupset \begin{array}{l} \llap{--}P(a) \\ \llap{--}\Psi(a) \end{array}$$

means: 'no meaning can be given to a such that $P(a)$ and $\Psi(a)$ p. 24] could both be affirmed.' We may thus render it as 'what has the property Ψ has not the property P' or 'no Ψ is a P.'

$$\vdash\vdash \overset{a}{\smile} \sqsupset \begin{array}{l} \llap{--}P(a) \\ \llap{--}\Lambda(a) \end{array}$$

denies $-\overset{a}{\smile} \sqsupset \begin{array}{l} P(a) \\ \Lambda(a) \end{array}$ and may therefore be rendered as 'some Λs are not Ps.'

$$\vdash\vdash \overset{a}{\smile} \sqsupset\sqsupset \begin{array}{l} \llap{--}P(a) \\ \llap{--}M(a) \end{array}$$

denies that no M is a P and thus means 'some Ms are Ps'* or 'it is possible for an M to be a P.' . . .

---

* The word 'some' must here always be understood to include the case 'one.' One might say more lengthily: 'some, or at least one.'

FUNCTION AND CONCEPT

An address given to the *Jenaische Gesellschaft für Medicin und Naturwissenschaft*, January 9, 1891

RATHER a long time ago* I had the honour of addressing this Society about the symbolic system that I entitled *Begriffsschrift*. To-day I should like to throw light upon the subject from another side, and tell you about some supplementations and new conceptions, whose necessity has occurred to me since then. There can here be no question of setting forth my ideography [*Begriffsschrift*] in its entirety, but only of elucidating some fundamental ideas.

My starting-point is what is called a function in mathematics. The original reference of this word was not so wide as that which it has since obtained; it will be well to begin by dealing with this first usage, and only then consider the later extensions. I shall for the moment be speaking only of functions of a single argument. The first place where a scientific expression appears with a clear-cut reference is where it is required for the statement p. 2] of a law. This case arose, as regards the function, upon the discovery of higher Analysis. Here for the first time it was a matter of setting forth laws holding for functions in general. So we must go back to the time when higher Analysis was discovered, if we want to know what the word 'function' was originally taken to mean. The answer that we are likely to get to this question is: 'A function of x was taken to be a mathematical expression containing x, a formula containing the letter x.'

Thus, e.g., the expression

$$2 x^3 + x$$

would be a function of x, and

$$2.2^3 + 2$$

would be a function of 2. This answer cannot satisfy us, for here no distinction is made between form and content, sign and thing

* On January 10, 1879, and January 27, 1882.

signified; a mistake, admittedly, that is very often met with in mathematical works, even those of celebrated authors. I have already pointed out on a previous occasion* the defects of the current formal theories in arithmetic. We there have talk about signs that neither have nor are meant to have any content, but nevertheless properties are ascribed to them which are unintelligible except as belonging to the content of a sign. So also here; p. 3] a mere expression, the form for a content, cannot be the heart of the matter; only the content itself can be that. Now what is the content of '$2.2^3 + 2$'? What does it stand for? The same thing as '18' or '3.6.' What is expressed in the equation '$2.2^3 + 2 = 18$' is that the right-hand complex of signs has the same reference as the left-hand one, I must here combat the view that, e.g., $2 + 5$ and $3 + 4$ are equal but not the same. This view is grounded in the same confusion of form and content, sign and thing signified. It is as though one wanted to regard the sweet-smelling violet as differing from *Viola odorata* because the names sound different. Difference of sign cannot by itself be a sufficient ground for difference of the thing signified. The only reason why in our case the matter is less obvious is that the reference of the numeral 7 is not anything perceptible to the senses. There is at present a very widespread tendency not to recognize as an object anything that cannot be perceived by means of the senses; this leads here to numerals' being taken to be numbers, the proper objects of our discussion;† and then, I admit, 7 and $2 + 5$ would indeed be different. But such a conception p. 4] is untenable, for we cannot speak of any arithmetical properties of numbers whatsoever without going back to what the signs stand for. For example, the property belonging to 1, of being the result of multiplying itself by itself, would be a mere myth; for no microscopical or chemical investigation, however far it was carried, could ever detect this property in the possession of the innocent character that we call a figure one. Perhaps there is talk of a definition; but no definition is creative in the sense of being able to endow a thing with properties that

---

* Die Grundlagen der Arithmetik, Breslau, 1884; Sitzungsberichte der Jenaischen Gesellschaft für Medicin und Naturwissenschaft, 1885, meeting of July 17th.

† Cf. the essays: Zählen und Messen erkenntnistheoretisch betrachtet, by H. von Helmholtz, and Ueber den Zahlbegriff, by Leopold Kronecker (Philosophische Aufsätze. Eduard Zeller zu seinen fünfzigjährigen Doctorjubiläum gewidmet, Leipzig, 1687).

it has not already got—apart from the one property of expressing and signifying something in virtue of the definition.* The characters we call numerals have, on the other hand, physical and chemical properties depending on the writing material. One could imagine the introduction some day of quite new numerals, just as, e.g., the Arabic numerals superseded the Roman. Nobody is seriously going to suppose that in this way we should get quite new numbers, quite new arithmetical objects, with properties still to be investigated. Thus we must distinguish between numerals and what they stand for; and if so, we shall have to recognize that the expressions '2,' '1 + 1,' '3 − 1,' '6:3' p. 5] stand for the same thing, for it is quite inconceivable where the difference between them could lie. Perhaps you say: 1 + 1 is a sum, but 6:3 is a quotient. But what is 6:3? The number that when multiplied by 3 gives the result 6. We say '*the* number,' not 'a number'; by using the definite article, we indicate that there is only a single number. Now we have:

$$(1 + 1) + (1 + 1) + (1 + 1) = 6,$$

and thus (1 + 1) is the very number that was designated as (6:3). The different expressions correspond to different conceptions and aspects, but nevertheless always to the same thing. Otherwise the equation $x^2 = 4$ would not just have the roots 2 and −2, but also the root (1 + 1) and countless others, all of them different, even if they resembled one another in a certain respect. By recognizing only two real roots, we are rejecting the view that the sign of equality does not stand for complete coincidence but only for partial agreement. If we adhere to this truth, we see that the expressions:

$$'2.1^3 + 1,'$$
$$'2.2^3 + 2,'$$
$$'2.4^3 + 4,'$$

stand for numbers, viz. 3, 18, 132. So if the function were really the reference of a mathematical expression, it would just be a number; and nothing new would have been gained for arithmetic [by speaking of functions]. Admittedly, people who use the word

* In definition it is always a matter of associating with a sign a sense or a reference. Where sense and reference are missing, we cannot properly speak either of a sign or of a definition.

p. 6] 'function' ordinarily have in mind expressions in which a number is just indicated indefinitely by the letter x, e.g.

$$'2.x^3 + x';$$

but that makes no difference; for this expression likewise just indicates a number indefinitely, and it makes no essential difference whether I write it down or just write down 'x.'

All the same, it is precisely by the notation that uses 'x' to indicate [a number] indefinitely that we are led to the right conception. People call x the argument, and recognize the same function again in

$$'2.1^3 + 1,'$$
$$'2.4^3 + 4,'$$
$$'2.5^3 + 5,'$$

only with different arguments, viz. 1, 4, and 5. From this we may discern that it is the common element of these expressions that contains the essential peculiarity of a function; i.e. what is present in

$$'2.x^3 + x'$$

over and above the letter 'x.' We could write this somewhat as follows:

$$'2.(\ )^3 + (\ ).'$$

I am concerned to show that the argument does not belong with the function, but goes together with the function to make up a complete whole; for the function by itself must be called incomplete, in need of supplementation, or 'unsaturated.' And in this respect functions differ fundamentally from numbers. Since such is the essence of the function, we can explain why, p. 7] on the one hand, we recognize the same function in '$2.1^3 + 1$' and '$2.2^3 + 2$,' even though these expressions stand for different numbers, whereas, on the other hand, we do not find one and the same function in '$2.1^3 + 1$' and '$4 - 1$' in spite of their equal numerical values. Moreover, we now see how people are easily led to regard the form of the expression as what is essential to the function. We recognize the function in the expression by imagining the latter as split up, and the possibility of thus splitting it up is suggested by its structure.

The two parts into which the mathematical expression is thus split up, the sign of the argument and the expression of the function, are dissimilar; for the argument is a number, a whole complete in itself, as the function is not. (We may compare this with the division of a line by a point. One is inclined in that case to count the dividing-point along with both segments; but if we want to make a clean division, i.e. so as not to count anything twice over or leave anything out, then we may only count the dividing-point along with one segment. This segment thus becomes fully complete in itself, and may be compared to the argument; whereas the other is lacking in something—viz. the dividing-point, which one may call its endpoint, does not belong to it. Only by completing it with this endpoint, or with a line that has two endpoints, do we get from it something entire.) For instance, if I say 'the function $2.x^3 + x$,' x must not p. 8] be considered as belonging to the function; this letter only serves to indicate the kind of supplementation that is needed; it enables one to recognize the places where the sign for the argument must go in.

We give the name 'the value of a function for an argument' to the result of completing the function with the argument. Thus, e.g., 3 is the value of the function $2.x^3 + x$ for the argument 1, since we have: $2.1^3 + 1 = 3$.

There are functions, such as $2 + x - x$ or $2 + 0.x$, whose value is always the same, whatever the argument; we have $2 = 2 + x - x$ and $2 = 2 + 0.x$. Now if we counted the argument as belonging with the function, we should hold that the number 2 is this function. But this is wrong. Even though here the value of the function is always 2, the function itself must nevertheless be distinguished from 2; for the expression for a function must always show one or more places that are intended to be filled up with the sign of the argument.

The method of analytic geometry supplies us with a means of intuitively representing the values of a function for different arguments. If we regard the argument as the numerical value of an abscissa, and the corresponding value of the function as the numerical value of the ordinate of a point, we obtain a set of points that presents itself to intuition (in ordinary cases) as a curve. Any point on the curve corresponds to an argument together with the associated value of the function.

p. 9] Thus, e.g.,

$$y = x^2 - 4x$$

yields a parabola; here 'y' indicates the value of the function and the numerical value of the ordinate, and 'x' similarly indicates the argument and the numerical value of the abscissa. If we compare with this the function

$$x(x - 4),$$

we find that they have always the same value for the same argument. We have generally:

$$x^2 - 4x = x(x - 4),$$

whatever number we take for x. Thus the curve we get from

$$y = x^2 - 4x$$

is the same as the one that arises out of

$$y = x(x - 4).$$

I express this as follows: the function $x(x - 4)$ has the same range of values as the function $x^2 - 4x$.

If we write

$$x^2 - 4x = x(x - 4),$$

we have not put one function equal to the other, but only the values of one equal to those of the other. And if we so understand this equation that it is to hold whatever argument may be substituted for x, then we have thus expressed that an equality holds generally. But we can also say: 'the value-range of the p. 10] function $x(x - 4)$ is equal to that of the function $x^2 - 4x$,' and here we have an equality between ranges of values. The possibility of regarding the equality holding generally between values of functions as a [particular] equality, viz. an equality between ranges of values, is, I think, indemonstrable; it must be taken to be a fundamental law of logic.*

We may further introduce a brief notation for the value-range of a function. To this end I replace the sign of the argument in the expression for the function by a Greek vowel, enclose the

---

* In many phrases of ordinary mathematical terminology, the word 'function' certainly corresponds to what I have here called the value-range of a function. But function, in the sense of the word employed here, is the logically prior [notion].

whole in brackets, and prefix to it the same Greek letter with a smooth breathing. Accordingly, e.g.,

$$\grave{\epsilon}\left(\epsilon^2 - 4\epsilon\right)$$

is the value-range of the function $x^2 - 4x$ and

$$\grave{a}\left(a.(a - 4)\right)$$

is the value-range of the function $x(x - 4)$, so that in

$$'\grave{\epsilon}(\epsilon^2 - 4\epsilon) = \grave{a}(a.(a - 4))'$$

we have the expression for: the first range of values is the same as the second. A different choice of Greek letters is made on purpose, in order to indicate that there is nothing that obliges us to take the same one.

p. 11] If we understand

$$'x^2 - 4x = x(x - 4)'$$

in the same sense as before, this expresses the same sense, but in a different way. It presents the sense as an equality holding generally; whereas the newly-introduced expression is simply an equation, and its right side, and equally its left side, stands for something complete in itself. In

$$'x^2 - 4x = x(x - 4)'$$

the left side considered in isolation indicates a number only indefinitely, and the same is true of the right side. If we just had '$x^2 - 4x$' we could write instead '$y^2 - 4y$' without altering the sense; for 'y' like 'x' indicates a number only indefinitely. But if we combine the two sides to form an equation, we must choose the same letter for both sides, and we thus express something that is not contained in the left side by itself, nor in the right side, nor in the 'equals' sign; viz. generality. Admittedly what we express is the generality of an equality; but primarily it is a generality.

Just as we indicate a number indefinitely by a letter, in order to express generality, we also need letters to indicate a function indefinitely. To this end people ordinarily use the letters f and F, thus: '$f(x)$,' '$F(x)$,' where 'x' replaces the argument. Here the need of the function for supplementation is expressed by the fact p. 12] that the letter f or F carries along with it a pair of brackets;

the space between these is meant to receive the sign for the argument. Thus

$$\grave{\epsilon}\, F(\epsilon)$$

indicates the value-range of a function that is left undetermined.

Now how has the reference of the word 'function' been extended by the progress of science? We can distinguish two directions in which this has happened.

In the first place, the field of mathematical operations that serve for constructing functions has been extended. Besides addition, multiplication, exponentiation, and their converses, the various means of transition to the limit have been introduced —to be sure, without people's being always clearly aware that they were thus adopting something essentially new. People have gone further still, and have actually been obliged to resort to ordinary language, because the symbolic language of Analysis failed; e.g. when they were speaking of a function whose value is 1 for rational and 0 for irrational arguments.

Secondly, the field of possible arguments and values for functions has been extended by the admission of complex numbers. In conjunction with this, the sense of the expressions 'sum,' 'product,' etc., had to be defined more widely.

In both directions I go still further. I begin by adding to the signs $+$, $-$, etc., which serve for constructing a functional p. 13] expression, also signs such as $=$, $>$, $<$, so that I can speak, e.g., of the function $x^2 = 1$, where x takes the place of the argument as before. The first question that arises here is what the values of this function are for different arguments. Now if we replace x successively by $-1, 0, 1, 2$, we get:

$$(-1)^2 = 1,$$
$$0^2 = 1,$$
$$1^2 = 1,$$
$$2^2 = 1.$$

Of these equations the first and third are true, the others false. I now say: 'the value of our function is a truth-value' and distinguish between the truth-values of what is true and what is false. I call the first, for short, the True; and the second, the False. Consequently, e.g., '$2^2 = 4$' stands for the True as, say,

'2^2' stands for 4. And '$2^2 = 1$' stands for the False. Accordingly

$$'2^2 = 4,'\ '2 > 1,'\ '2^4 = 4^2,'$$

stand for the same thing, viz. the True, so that in

$$(2^2 = 4) = (2 > 1)$$

we have a correct equation.

The objection here suggests itself that '$2^2 = 4$' and '$2 > 1$' nevertheless make quite different assertions, express quite different thoughts; but likewise '$2^4 = 4^2$' and '$4.4 = 4^2$' express different thoughts; and yet we can replace '2^4' by '4.4,' since both signs have the same reference. Consequently, '$2^4 = 4^2$' and '$4.4 = 4^2$' p. 14] likewise have the same reference. We see from this that from identity of reference there does not follow identity of the thought [expressed]. If we say 'the Evening Star is a planet with a shorter period of revolution than the Earth,' the thought we express is other than in the sentence 'the Morning Star is a planet with a shorter period of revolution than the Earth'; for somebody who does know that the Morning Star is the Evening Star might regard one as true and the other as false. And yet both sentences must have the same reference; for it is just a matter of interchanging the words 'Evening Star' and 'Morning Star,' which have the same reference, i.e. are proper names of the same heavenly body. We must distinguish between sense and reference. '2^4' and '4^2' certainly have the same reference, i.e. they are proper names of the same number; but they have not the same sense; consequently, '$2^4 = 4^2$' and '$4.4 = 4^2$' have the same reference, but not the same sense (which means, in this case: they do not contain the same thought).*

Thus, just as we write:

$$'2^4 = 4.4'$$

we may also write with equal justification

$$'(2^4 = 4^2) = (4.4 = 4^2)'$$
$$\text{and } '(2^2 = 4) = (2 > 1).'$$

* I do not fail to see that this way of putting it may at first seem arbitrary and artificial, and that it would be desirable to establish my view by going further into the matter. Cf. my forthcoming essay *Ueber Sinn und Bedeutung* ['Sense and Reference'] in the *Zeitschrift für Philosophie und phil. Kritik.*

p. 15] It might further be asked: What, then, is the point of admitting the signs =, >, <, into the field of those that help to build up a functional expression? Nowadays, it seems, more and more supporters are being won by the view that arithmetic is a further development of logic; that a more rigorous establishment of arithmetical laws reduces them to purely logical laws and to such laws alone. I too am of this opinion, and I base upon it the requirement that the symbolic language of arithmetic must be expanded into a logical symbolism. I shall now have to indicate how this is done in our present case.

We saw that the value of our function $x^2 = 1$ is always one of the two truth-values. Now if for a definite argument, e.g. $- 1$, the value of the function is the True, we can express this as follows: 'the number $- 1$ has the property that its square is 1'; or, more briefly, '$- 1$ is a square root of 1'; or, '$- 1$ falls under the concept: square root of 1.' If the value of the function $x^2 = 1$ for an argument, e.g. for 2, is the False, we can express this as follows: '2 is not a square root of 1' or '2 does not fall under the concept: square root of 1.' We thus see how closely that which is called a concept in logic is connected with what we call a function. Indeed, we may say at once: a concept is a function whose value is always a truth-value. Again, the value of the function

$$(x + 1)^2 = 2(x + 1)$$

p. 16] is always a truth-value. We get the True as its value, e.g., for the argument $- 1$, and this can also be expressed thus: $- 1$ is a number less by 1 than a number whose square is equal to its double. This expresses the fact that $- 1$ falls under a concept. Now the functions

$$x^2 = 1 \text{ and } (x + 1)^2 = 2(x + 1)$$

always have the same value for the same argument, viz. the True for the arguments $- 1$ and $+ 1$, and the False for all other arguments. According to our previous conventions we shall also say that these functions have the same range of values, and express this in symbols as follows:

$$\dot\epsilon(\epsilon^2 = 1) = \dot a((a + 1)^2 = 2(a + 1)).$$

In logic this is called identity of the extension of the concepts.

Hence we can designate as an extension the value-range of a function whose value for every argument is a truth-value.

We shall not stop at equations and inequalities. The linguistic form of equations is a statement. A statement contains (or at least purports to contain) a thought as its sense; and this thought is in general true or false; i.e. it has in general a truth-value, which must be regarded as the reference of the sentence, just as (say) the number 4 is the reference of the expression '2 + 2,' or London of the expression 'the capital of England.'

p. 17] Statements in general, just like equations or inequalities or expressions in Analysis, can be imagined to be split up into two parts; one complete in itself, and the other in need of supplementation, or 'unsaturated.' Thus, e.g., we split up the sentence

'Caesar conquered Gaul'

into 'Caesar' and 'conquered Gaul.' The second part is 'unsaturated'—it contains an empty place; only when this place is filled up with a proper name, or with an expression that replaces a proper name, does a complete sense appear. Here too I give the name 'function' to what this 'unsaturated' part stands for. In this case the argument is Caesar.

We see that here we have undertaken to extend [the application of the term] in the other direction, viz. as regards what can occur as an argument. Not merely numbers, but objects in general, are now admissible; and here persons must assuredly be counted as objects. The two truth-values have already been introduced as possible values of a function; we must go further and admit objects without restriction as values of functions. To get an example of this, let us start, e.g., with the expression

'the capital of the German Empire.'

This obviously takes the place of a proper name, and stands for an object. If we now split it up into the parts

p. 18] 'the capital of' and 'the German Empire'

where I count the [German] genitive form as going with the first part, then this part is 'unsaturated,' whereas the other is complete in itself. So in accordance with what I said before, I call

'the capital of x'

the expression of a function. If we take the German Empire as the argument, we get Berlin as the value of the function.

When we have thus admitted objects without restriction as arguments and values of functions, the question arises what it is that we are here calling an object. I regard a regular definition as impossible, since we have here something too simple to admit of logical analysis. It is only possible to indicate what is meant. Here I can only say briefly: An object is anything that is not a function, so that an expression for it does not contain any empty place.

A statement contains no empty place, and therefore we must regard what it stands for as an object. But what a statement stands for is a truth-value. Thus the two truth-values are objects.

Earlier on we presented equations between ranges of values, e.g.:

$$`\acute{\epsilon}(\epsilon^2 - 4\epsilon) = \acute{a}(a(a - 4)).'$$

We can split this up into $`\acute{\epsilon}(\epsilon^2 - 4\epsilon)'$ and $`(\quad) = \acute{a}(a(a - 4)).'$ This latter part needs supplementation, since on the left of the p. 19] 'equals' sign it contains an empty place. The first part, $`\acute{\epsilon}(\epsilon^2 - 4\epsilon),'$ is fully complete in itself and thus stands for an object. Value-ranges of functions are objects, whereas functions themselves are not. We gave the name 'value-range' also to $\acute{\epsilon}(\epsilon^2 = 1)$, but we could also have termed it the extension of the concept: square root of 1. Extensions of concepts likewise are objects, although concepts themselves are not.

After thus extending the field of things that may be taken as arguments, we must get more exact specifications as to what the signs already in use stand for. So long as the only objects dealt with in arithmetic are the integers, the letters a and b in $'a + b'$ indicate only integers; the plus-sign need be defined only between integers. Every extension of the field to which the objects indicated by a and b belong obliges us to give a new definition of the plus-sign. It seems to be demanded by scientific rigour that we should have provisos against an expression's possibly coming to have no reference; we must see to it that we never perform calculations with empty signs in the belief that we are dealing with objects. People have in the past carried out invalid procedures with divergent infinite series. It is thus necessary to lay down rules from which it follows, e.g., what

$$\text{`}\odot + 1\text{'}$$

stands for, if '$\odot$' is to stand for the Sun. What rules we lay down p. 20] is a matter of comparative indifference; but it is essential that we should do so—that '$a + b$' should always have a reference, whatever signs for definite objects may be inserted in place of 'a' and 'b.' This involves the requirement as regards concepts, that, for any argument, they shall have a truth-value as their value; that it shall be determinate, for any object, whether it falls under the concept or not. In other words: as regards concepts we have a requirement of sharp delimitation; if this were not satisfied it would be impossible to set forth logical laws about them. For any argument x for which '$x + 1$' were devoid of reference, the function $x + 1 = 10$ would likewise have no value, and thus no truth-value either, so that the concept:

'what gives the result 10 when increased by 1'

would have no sharp boundaries. The requirement of the sharp delimitation of concepts thus carries along with it this requirement for functions in general that they must have a value for every argument.

We have so far considered truth-values only as values of functions, not as arguments. By what I have just said, we must get a value of a function when we take a truth-value as the argument; but as regards the signs already in common use, the only point, in most cases, of a rule to this effect is that there should *be* a rule; it does not much matter what is determined upon. But now we must deal with certain functions that are of importance to us precisely when their argument is a truth-value.

p. 21] I introduce the following as such a function

$$\text{---} x;$$

I lay down the rule that the value of this function shall be the True if the True is taken as argument, and that contrariwise, in all other cases the value of this function is the False—i.e. both when the argument is the False and when it is not a truth-value at all. Accordingly, e.g.

$$—— 1 + 3 = 4$$

is the True, whereas both

$$— 1 + 3 = 5$$

and also

$$—— 4$$

are the False. Thus this function has as its value the argument itself, when that is a truth-value. I used to call this horizontal stroke the content-stroke (*Inhaltsstrich*)—a name that no longer seems to me appropriate. I now wish to call it simply the horizontal.

If we write down an equation or inequality, e.g. $5 > 4$, we ordinarily wish at the same time to express a judgment; in our example, we want to assert that 5 is greater than 4. According to the view I am here presenting, '$5 > 4$' and '$1 + 3 = 5$' just give us expressions for truth-values, without making any assertion. This separation of the act from the subject-matter of judgment seems to be indispensable; for otherwise we could not express a mere supposition—the putting of a case without a p. 22] simultaneous judgment as to its arising or not. We thus need a special sign in order to be able to assert something. To this end I make use of a vertical stroke at the left end of the horizontal, so that, e.g., by writing

$$\vdash—— 2 + 3 = 5$$

we assert that $2 + 3$ equals 5. Thus here we are not just writing down a truth-value, as in

$$2 + 3 = 5,$$

but also at the same time saying that it is the True.*

The next simplest function, we may say, is the one whose value is the False for just those arguments for which the value of $—— x$ is the True, and, conversely, is the True for the arguments for which the value of $—— x$ is the False. I symbolize it thus:

$$\multimap x,$$

---

* The assertion sign (*Urtheilsstrich*) cannot be used to construct a functional expression; for it does not serve, in conjunction with other signs, to designate an object. '$\vdash—— 2 + 3 = 5$' does not designate anything; it asserts something.

and here I call the little vertical stroke the stroke of negation. I conceive of this as a function with the argument —— x:

$$(\text{—}_\top x) = (\text{—}_\top (\text{——} x))$$

where I imagine the two horizontal strokes to be fused together. But we also have:

$$(\text{——} (\text{—}_\top x)) = (\text{—}_\top x),$$

p. 23] since the value of $\text{—}_\top x$ is always a truth-value. I thus regard the bits of the stroke in ' $\text{-}_\top x$ ' to the right and to the left of the stroke of negation as horizontals, in the sense of the word that I defined previously. Accordingly, e.g.:

$$\text{—}_\top 2^2 = 5$$

stands for the True, and we may add the assertion-sign:

$$\vdash_\top 2^2 = 5;$$

and in this we assert that $2^2 = 5$ is not the True, or that 2^2 is not 5. But moreover

$$\text{—}_\top 2$$

is the True, since —— 2 is the False:

$$\vdash_\top 2$$

i.e. 2 is not the True.

My way of presenting generality can best be seen in an example. Suppose what we have to express is that every object is equal to itself. In

$$x = x$$

we have a function, whose argument is indicated by 'x.' We now have to say that the value of this function is always the True, whatever we take as argument. I now take the sign

$$\text{—}\overset{a}{\smile}\text{—}f(a)$$

to mean the True when the function $f(x)$ always has the True as its value, whatever the argument may be; in all other cases

p. 24] $$\text{—}\overset{a}{\smile}\text{—}f(a)$$

is to stand for the False. For our function $x = x$ we get the first case. Thus

$$-\!\underset{\smile}{\overset{a}{}}\!\!-f(a)$$

is the True; and we write this as follows:

$$\vdash\!\underset{\smile}{\overset{a}{}}\!\!-a = a$$

The horizontal strokes to the right and to the left of the concavity are to be regarded as horizontals in our sense. Instead of 'a,' any other Gothic letter could be chosen; except those which are to serve as letters for a function, like f and F.

This notation affords the possibility of negating generality, as in

$$-\!\!\top\!\underset{\smile}{\overset{a}{}}\!\!-a^2 = 1.$$

That is to say, $-\!\underset{\smile}{\overset{a}{}}\!\!-a^2 = 1$ is the False, since not every argument makes the value of the function $x^2 = 1$ to be the True. (Thus, e.g., we get $2^2 = 1$ for the argument 2, and this is the False.) Now if $-\!\underset{\smile}{\overset{a}{}}\!\!-a^2 = 1$ is the False, then $-\!\!\top\!\underset{\smile}{\overset{a}{}}\!\!-a^2 = 1$ is the True, according to the rule that we laid down previously for the stroke of negation. Thus we have

$$\vdash\!\!\top\!\underset{\smile}{\overset{a}{}}\!\!-a^2 = 1;$$

i.e. 'not every object is a square root of 1,' or 'there are objects that are not square roots of 1.'

p. 25] Can we also express: there are square roots of 1? Certainly: we need only take, instead of the function $x^2 = 1$, the function

$$-\!\!\top\! x^2 = 1.$$

By fusing together the horizontals in

$$-\!\underset{\smile}{\overset{a}{}}\!\!-\;-\!\!\top\; a^2 = 1$$

we get

$$-\!\underset{\smile}{\overset{a}{}}\!\!\top\! a^2 = 1.$$

This stands for the False, since not every argument makes the value of the function

$$—\!\!\top— x^2 = 1$$

to be the True. E.g.:

$$—\!\!\top— 1^2 = 1$$

is the False, for $1^2 = 1$ is the True. Now since

$$—\!\!\underset{a}{\smile}\!\!\top— a^2 = 1$$

is thus the False,

$$—\!\!\top\!\!\underset{a}{\smile}\!\!\top— a^2 = 1$$

is the True:

$$\vdash\!\!\top\!\!\underset{a}{\smile}\!\!\top— a^2 = 1;$$

i.e. 'not every argument makes the value of the function

$$—\!\!\top— x^2 = 1$$

to be the True,' or: 'not every argument makes the value of the function $x^2 = 1$ to be the False,' or: 'there is at least one square root of 1.'

At this point there may follow a few examples in symbols and words.

$$\vdash\!\!\top\!\!\underset{a}{\smile}\!\!\top— a \geqq 0,$$

there is at least one positive number;

p. 26]
$$\vdash\!\!\top\!\!\underset{a}{\smile}\!\!\top— a < 0,$$

there is at least one negative number;

$$\vdash\!\!\top\!\!\underset{a}{\smile}\!\!\top— a^3 - 3a^2 + 2a = 0,$$

there is at least one root of the equation

$$x^3 - 3x^2 + 2x = 0.$$

From this we may see how to express existential sentences,

which are so important. If we use the functional letter f as an indefinite indication of a concept, then

$$\vdash\!\!\overset{a}{\rule[0.5ex]{1.5em}{0.4pt}}\!\cup\!\rule[0.5ex]{1.5em}{0.4pt}\, f(a)$$

gives us the form that includes the last examples (if we abstract from the assertion-sign). The expressions

$$\overset{a}{\rule[0.5ex]{1.5em}{0.4pt}}\!\cup\!\rule[0.5ex]{1.5em}{0.4pt}\, a^2 = 1, \qquad \overset{a}{\rule[0.5ex]{1.5em}{0.4pt}}\!\cup\!\rule[0.5ex]{1.5em}{0.4pt}\, a \geq 0,$$

$$\overset{a}{\rule[0.5ex]{1.5em}{0.4pt}}\!\cup\!\rule[0.5ex]{1.5em}{0.4pt}\, a < 0, \qquad \overset{a}{\rule[0.5ex]{1.5em}{0.4pt}}\!\cup\!\rule[0.5ex]{1.5em}{0.4pt}\, a^2 - 3a^2 + 2a = 0$$

arise from this form in a manner analogous to that in which x^2 gives rise to '1^2,' '2^2,' '3^2.' Now just as in x^2 we have a function whose argument is indicated by 'x,' I also conceive of

$$\overset{a}{\rule[0.5ex]{1.5em}{0.4pt}}\!\cup\!\rule[0.5ex]{1.5em}{0.4pt}\, f(a)$$

as the expression of a function whose argument is indicated by 'f.' Such a function is obviously a fundamentally different one from those we have dealt with so far; for only a function can occur as its argument. Now just as functions are fundamentally different from objects, so also functions whose arguments are and must be functions are fundamentally different from functions whose arguments are objects and cannot be anything else. I call p. 27] the latter first-level, the former second-level, functions. In the same way, I distinguish between first-level and second-level concepts.* Second-level functions have actually long been used in Analysis; e.g. definite integrals (if we regard the function to be integrated as the argument).

I will now add something about functions with two arguments. We get the expression for a function by splitting up the complex sign for an object into a 'saturated' and an 'unsaturated' part. Thus, we split up this sign for the True,

$$3 > 2,$$

* Cf. my *Grundlagen der Arithmetik*, Breslau, 1884. I there used the term 'second-order' instead of 'second-level.' The ontological proof of God's existence suffers from the fallacy of treating existence as a first-level concept.

into '3' and '$x > 2$.' We can further split up the 'unsaturated' part '$x > 2$' in the same way, into '2' and

$$x > y,$$

where 'y' enables us to recognize the empty place previously filled up by '2.' In

$$x > y$$

we have a function with two arguments, one indicated by 'x' and the other by 'y'; and in

$$3 > 2$$

p. 28] we have the value of this function for the arguments 3 and 2. We have here a function whose value is always a truth-value. We called such functions of one argument concepts; we call such functions of two arguments relations. Thus we have relations also, e.g., in

$$x^2 + y^2 = 9$$

and in

$$x^2 + y^2 > 9,$$

whereas the function

$$x^2 + y^2$$

has numbers as values. We shall therefore not call this a relation.

At this point I may introduce a function not peculiar to arithmetic. The value of the function

is to be the False if we take the True as the y-argument and at the same time take some object that is not the True as the x-argument; in all other cases the value of this function is to be the True. The lower horizontal stroke, and the two bits that the upper one is split into by the vertical, are to be regarded as horizontals [in our sense]. Consequently, we can always regard as the arguments of our function —— x and —— y, i.e. truth-values.

Among functions of one argument we distinguished first-level and second-level ones. Here, a greater multiplicity is possible.

A function of two arguments may be of the same level in relation
p. 29] to them, or of different levels; there are equal-levelled
and unequal-levelled functions. Those we have dealt with up to
now were equal-levelled. An example of an unequal-levelled
function is the differential quotient, if we take the arguments
to be the function that is to be differentiated and the argument
for which it is differentiated; or the definite integral, so long as
we take as arguments the function to be integrated and the upper
limit. Equal-levelled functions can again be divided into first-
level and second-level ones. An example of a second-level one is

$$F(f(\mathrm{I})),$$

where 'F' and 'f' indicate the arguments.

In regard to second-level functions with one argument, we
must make a distinction, according as the role of this argument
can be played by a function of one or of two arguments; for a
function of one argument is essentially so different from one with
two arguments that the one function cannot occur as an argument
in the same place as the other. Some second-level functions of
one argument require that this should be a function with one
argument; others, that it should be a function with two arguments; and these two classes are sharply divided.

p. 30] is an example of a second-level function with one
argument, which requires that this should be a function of two
arguments. The letter F here indicates the argument, and the
two places, separated by a comma, within the brackets that follow
'F' bring it to our notice that F represents a function with two
arguments.

For functions of two arguments there arises a still greater
multiplicity.

If we look back from here over the development of arithmetic,
we discern an advance from level to level. At first people did
calculations with individual numbers, I, 3, etc.

$$2 + 3 = 5, 2.3 = 6$$

are theorems of this sort. Then they went on to more general laws that hold good for all numbers. What corresponds to this in symbolism is the transition to the literal notation.

A theorem of this sort is

$$(a + b)c = a.c + b.c.$$

At this stage they had got to the point of dealing with individual functions; but were not yet using the word, in its mathematical sense, and had not yet formed the conception of what it now stands for. The next higher level was the recognition of general laws about functions, accompanied by the coinage of the technical term 'function.' What corresponds to this in symbolism is the introduction of letters like f, F, to indicate functions indefinitely. A theorem of this sort is

$$\frac{df(x).F(x)}{dx} = \frac{F(x).df(x)}{dx} + \frac{f(x).dF(x)}{dx}$$

p. 31] Now at this point people had particular second-level functions, but lacked the conception of what we have called second-level functions. By forming that, we make the next step forward. One might think that this would go on. But probably this last step is already not so rich in consequences as the earlier ones; for instead of second-level functions one can deal, in further advances, with first-level functions—as shall be shown elsewhere. But this docs not banish from the world the difference between first-level and second-level functions; for it is not made arbitrarily, but founded deep in the nature of things.

Again, instead of functions of two arguments we can deal with functions of a single but complex argument; but the distinction between functions of one and of two arguments still holds in all its sharpness.

ON CONCEPT AND OBJECT

First published in the *Vierteljahrsschrift für wissenschaftliche Philosophie*, 16 (1892): 192-205

p. 192] IN a series of articles in this Quarterly on intuition and its psychical elaboration, Benno Kerry has several times referred to my *Grundlagen der Arithmetik* and other works of mine, sometimes agreeing and sometimes disagreeing with me. I cannot but be pleased at this, and I think the best way I can show my appreciation is to take up the discussion of the points he contests. This seems to me all the more necessary, because his opposition is at least partly based on a misunderstanding, which might be shared by others, of what I say about the concept; and because, even apart from this special occasion, the matter is important and difficult enough for a more thorough treatment than seemed to me suitable in my *Grundlagen*.

The word 'concept' is used in various ways; its sense is sometimes psychological, sometimes logical, and sometimes perhaps a confused mixture of both. Since this licence exists, it is natural to restrict it by requiring that when once a usage is adopted it shall be maintained. What I decided was to keep strictly to a purely logical use; the question whether this or that use is more appropriate is one that I should like to leave on one side, as of minor importance. Agreement about the mode of expression will easily be reached when once it is recognized that there is something that deserves a special term.

It seems to me that Kerry's misunderstanding results from his unintentionally confusing his own usage of the word 'concept' with mine. This readily gives rise to contradictions, for which my usage is not to blame.

p. 193] Kerry contests what he calls my definition of 'concept.' I would remark, in the first place, that my explanation is not meant as a proper definition. One cannot require that everything shall be defined, any more than one can require that a chemist shall decompose every substance. What is simple cannot be

42

decomposed, and what is logically simple cannot have a proper definition. Now something logically simple is no more given us at the outset than most of the chemical elements are; it is reached only by means of scientific work. If something has been discovered that is simple, or at least must count as simple for the time being, we shall have to coin a term for it, since language will not originally contain an expression that exactly answers. On the introduction of a name for something logically simple, a definition is not possible; there is nothing for it but to lead the reader or hearer, by means of hints, to understand the words as is intended.

Kerry wants to make out that the distinction between concept and object is not absolute. 'In a previous passage,' he says, 'I have myself expressed the opinion that the relation between the content of the concept and the concept-object is, in a certain respect, a peculiar and irreducible one; but this was in no way bound up with the view that the properties of being a concept and of being an object are mutually exclusive. The latter view no more follows from the former than it would follow, if, e.g., the relation of father and son were one that could not be further reduced, that a man could not be at once a father and a son (though of course not, e.g., father of the man whose son he was).'

Let us fasten on this simile. If there were, or had been, beings that were fathers but could not be sons, such beings would obviously be quite different in kind from all men who are sons. Now it is something like this that happens here. The concept (as I understand the word) is predicative.* On the other hand, a name of an object, a proper name, is quite incapable of being used as a grammatical predicate. This admittedly needs elucidation, otherwise it might appear false. Surely one can just as well assert of a thing that it is Alexander the Great, or is the number four, or is the planet Venus, as that it is green or is a mammal? p.194] If anybody thinks this, he is not distinguishing the usages of the word 'is.' In the last two examples it serves as a copula, as a mere verbal sign of predication. (In this sense [the German word *ist*] can sometimes be replaced by the mere personal suffix: cf. *dies*

---

* It is, in fact, the reference of a grammatical predicate.

Blatt ist grün and *dies Blatt grünt*.) We are here saying that something falls under a concept, and the grammatical predicate stands for this concept. In the first three examples, on the other hand, 'is' is used like the 'equals' sign in arithmetic, to express an equation.* In the sentence 'The morning star is Venus,' we have two proper names, 'morning star' and 'Venus,' for the same object. In the sentence 'the morning star is a planet' we have a proper name, 'the morning star,' and a concept-word, 'planet.' So far as language goes, no more has happened than that 'Venus' has been replaced by 'a planet'; but really the relation has become wholly different. An equation is reversible; an object's falling under a concept is an irreversible relation. In the sentence 'the morning star is Venus,' 'is' is obviously not the mere copula; its content is an essential part of the predicate, so that the word 'Venus' does not constitute the whole of the predicate.† One might say instead: 'the morning star is no other than Venus'; what was previously implicit in the single word 'is' is here set forth in four separate words, and in 'is no other than' the word 'is' now really is the mere copula. What is predicated here is thus not *Venus* but *no other than Venus*. These words stand for a concept; admittedly only one object falls under this, but such a concept must still always be distinguished from the object.‡ We have here a word 'Venus' that can never be a proper predicate, p. 195] although it can form part of a predicate. The reference§ of this word is thus something that can never occur as a concept, but only as an object. Kerry, too, would probably not wish to dispute that there is something of this kind. But this would mean admitting a distinction, which it is very important to recognize, between what can occur only as an object, and everything else. And this distinction would not be effaced even if it were true, as Kerry thinks it is, that there are concepts that can also be objects.

* I use the word 'equal' and the symbol ' = ' in the sense 'the same as,' 'no other than,' 'identical with.' Cf. E. Schroeder, *Vorlesungen ueber die Algebra der Logik* (Leipzig 1890), Vol. 1, § 1. Schroeder must however be criticized for not distinguishing two fundamentally different relations; the relation of an object to a concept it falls under, and the subordination of one concept to another. His remarks on the *Vollwurzel* are likewise open to objection. Schroeder's symbol ⧧ does not simply take the place of the copula.
† Cf. my *Grundlagen*, § 66, footnote.
‡ Cf. my *Grundlagen*, § 51.
§ Cf. my paper, 'On Sense and Reference' (*Ueber Sinn und Bedeutung*), shortly to appear in the *Zeitschrift für Phil. und phil. Kritik*.

There are, indeed, cases that seem to support his view. I myself
have indicated (in *Grundlagen*, § 53, *ad fin.*) that a concept may fall
under a higher concept—which, however, must not be confused
with one concept's being subordinate to another. Kerry does not
appeal to this; instead, he gives the following example: 'the
concept "horse" is a concept easily attained,' and thinks that the
concept 'horse' is an object, in fact one of the objects that fall
under the concept 'concept easily attained.' Quite so; the three
words 'the concept "horse"' do designate an object, but on that
very account they do not designate a concept, as I am using the
word. This is in full accord with the criterion I gave—that the
singular definite article always indicates an object, whereas the
indefinite article accompanies a concept-word.*

Kerry holds that no logical rules can be based on linguistic
distinctions; but my own way of doing this is something that
nobody can avoid who lays down such rules at all; for we cannot
come to an understanding with one another apart from language,
and so in the end we must always rely on other people's understanding words, inflexions, and sentence-construction in essentially the same way as ourselves. As I said before, I was not trying
to give a definition, but only hints; and to this end I appealed to
the general feeling for the German language. It is here very much
to my advantage that there is such good accord between the linguistic distinction and the real one. As regards the indefinite article
there are probably no exceptions to our rule at all for us to remark,
apart from obsolete formulas like *Ein edler Rath* ['Councillor'].
The matter is not so simple for the definite article, especially
p. 196] in the plural; but then my criterion does not relate to
this case. In the singular, so far as I can see, the matter is doubtful
only when a singular takes the place of a plural, as in the sentence
'the Turk besieged Vienna,' 'the horse is a four-legged animal.'
These cases are so easily recognizable as special ones that the
value of our rule is hardly impaired by their occurrence. It is
clear that in the first sentence 'the Turk' is the proper name of a
people. The second sentence is probably best regarded as expressing a universal judgment, say 'all horses are four-legged animals'
or 'all properly constituted horses are four-legged animals';

* *Grundlagen*, § 51; § 66, footnote; § 68, footnote on p. 80.

these will be discussed later.* Kerry calls my criterion unsuitable; for surely, he says, in the sentence 'the concept that I am now talking about is an individual concept' the name composed of the first eight words stands for a concept; but he is not taking the word 'concept' in my sense, and it is not in what I have laid down that the contradiction lies. But nobody can require that my mode of expression shall agree with Kerry's.

It must indeed be recognized that here we are confronted by an awkwardness of language, which I admit cannot be avoided, if we say that the concept *horse* is not a concept,† whereas, e.g., the city p. 197] of Berlin is a city, and the volcano Vesuvius is a volcano. Language is here in a predicament that justifies the departure from custom. The peculiarity of our case is indicated by Kerry himself, by means of the quotation-marks around 'horse'; I use italics to the same end. There was no reason to mark out the words 'Berlin' and 'Vesuvius' in a similar way. In logical discussions one quite often needs to assert something about a concept, and to express this in the form usual for such assertions—viz. to make what is asserted of the concept into the content of the grammatical predicate. Consequently, one would expect that the reference of the grammatical subject would be the concept; but the concept as such cannot play this part, in view of its predicative nature; it must first be converted into an object,‡ or, speaking more precisely, represented by an object. We

* Nowadays people seem inclined to exaggerate the scope of the statement that different linguistic expressions are never completely equivalent, that a word can never be exactly translated into another language. One might perhaps go even further, and say that the same word is never taken in quite the same way even by men who share a language. I will not enquire as to the measure of truth in these statements; I would only emphasize that nevertheless different expressions quite often have something in common, which I call the sense, or, in the special case of sentences, the thought. In other words, we must not fail to recognize that the same sense, the same thought, may be variously expressed; thus the difference does not here concern the sense, but only the apprehension, shading, or colouring of the thought, and is irrelevant for logic. It is possible for one sentence to give no more and no less information than another; and, for all the multiplicity of languages, mankind has a common stock of thoughts. If all transformation of the expression were forbidden on the plea that this would alter the content as well, logic would simply be crippled; for the task of logic can hardly be performed without trying to recognize the thought in its manifold guises. Moreover, all definitions would then have to be rejected as false.

† A similar thing happens when we say as regards the sentence 'this rose is red': The grammatical predicate 'is red' belongs to the subject 'this rose.' Here the words 'The grammatical predicate "is red" ' are not a grammatical predicate but a subject. By the very act of explicitly calling it a predicate, we deprive it of this property.

‡ Cf. my *Grundlagen*, p. x.

designate this object by prefixing the words 'the concept';
e.g.:

'The concept *man* is not empty.'

Here the first three words are to be regarded as a proper name,* which can no more be used predicatively than 'Berlin' or 'Vesuvius.' When we say 'Jesus falls under the concept *man*,' then, setting aside the copula, the predicate is:

'someone falling under the concept *man*'

and this means the same as:

'a man.'

But the phrase

'the concept *man*'

is only part of this predicate.

Somebody might urge, as against the predicative nature of the concept, that nevertheless we speak of a subject-concept. But even in such cases, e.g. in the sentence

'all mammals have red blood'

we cannot fail to recognize the predicative nature† of the concept; for we could say instead:

p. 198]   'whatever is a mammal has red blood'

or:

'if anything is a mammal, then it has red blood.'

When I wrote my *Grundlagen der Arithmetik*, I had not yet made the distinction between sense and reference;‡ and so, under the expression 'a possible content of judgment,' I was combining what I now designate by the distinctive words 'thought' and 'truth-value.' Consequently, I no longer entirely approve of the explanation I then gave (op. cit., p. 77), as regards its wording; my view is, however, still essentially the same. We may say in brief, taking 'subject' and 'predicate' in the linguistic sense: A

---

* I call anything a proper name if it is a sign for an object.

† What I call here the predicative nature of the concept is just a special case of the need of supplementation, the 'unsaturatedness,' that I gave as the essential feature of a function in my work *Function und Begriff* (Jena, 1891). It was there scarcely possible to avoid the expression 'the function $f(x)$,' although there too the difficulty arose that what this expression stands for is not a function.

‡ Cf. my essay 'On Sense and Reference' in the *Zeitschrift für Phil. und phil. Kritik*.

concept is the reference of a predicate; an object is something that can never be the whole reference of a predicate, but can be the reference of a subject. It must here be remarked that the words 'all,' 'any,' 'no,' 'some,' are prefixed to concept-words. In universal and particular affirmative and negative sentences, we are expressing relations between concepts; we use these words to indicate the special kind of relation. They are thus, logically speaking, not to be more closely associated with the concept-words that follow them, but are to be related to the sentence as a whole. It is easy to see this in the case of negation. If in the sentence

'all mammals are land-dwellers'

the phrase 'all mammals' expressed the logical subject of the predicate *are land-dwellers*, then in order to negate the whole sentence we should have to negate the predicate: 'are not land-dwellers.' Instead, we must put the 'not' in front of 'all'; from which it follows that 'all' logically belongs with the predicate. On the other hand, we do negate the sentence 'The concept *mammal* is subordinate to the concept *land-dweller*' by negating the predicate: 'is not subordinate to the concept *land-dweller.*'

If we keep it in mind that in my way of speaking expressions like 'the concept F' designate not concepts but objects, most of p. 199] Kerry's objections already collapse. If he thinks (cf. p. 281) that I have identified concept and extension of concept, he is mistaken; I merely expressed my view that in the expression 'the number that applies to the concept F is the extension of the concept *like-numbered to the concept F*' the words 'extension of the concept' could be replaced by 'concept.' Notice carefully that here the word 'concept' is combined with the definite article. Besides, this was only an incidental remark; I did not base anything upon it.

Thus Kerry does not succeed in filling the gap between concept and object. Someone might attempt, however, to make use of my own statements in this sense. I have said that to assign a number involves an assertion about a concept;* I speak of properties asserted of a concept, and I allow that a concept may fall under a higher one.† I have called existence a property of a

---

* *Grundlagen*, § 46.   † *Grundlagen*, § 53.

concept. How I mean this to be taken is best made clear by an example. In the sentence 'there is at least one square root of 4,' we have an assertion, not about (say) the definite number 2, nor about —2, but about a concept, *square root of 4*; viz. that it is not empty. But if I express the same thought thus: 'The concept *square root of 4* is realized,' then the first six words form the proper name of an object, and it is about this object that something is asserted. But notice carefully that what is asserted here is not the same thing as was asserted about the concept. This will be surprising only to somebody who fails to see that a thought can be split up in many ways, so that now one thing, now another, appears as subject or predicate. The thought itself does not yet determine what is to be regarded as the subject. If we say 'the subject of this judgment,' we do not designate anything definite unless at the same time we indicate a definite kind of analysis; as a rule, we do this in connexion with a definite wording. But we must never forget that different sentences may express the same thought. For example, the thought we are considering could also be taken as an assertion about the number 4:

'The number 4 has the property that there is something of which it is the square.'

Language has means of presenting now one, now another, part p. 200] of the thought as the subject; one of the most familiar is the distinction of active and passive forms. It is thus not impossible that one way of analysing a given thought should make it appear as a singular judgment; another, as a particular judgment; and a third, as a universal judgment. It need not then surprise us that the same sentence may be conceived as an assertion about a concept and also as an assertion about an object; only we must observe that what is asserted is different. In the sentence 'there is at least one square root of 4' it is impossible to replace the words 'square root of 4' by 'the concept *square root of 4*'; i.e. the assertion that suits the concept does not suit the object. Although our sentence does not present the concept as a subject, it asserts something about it; it can be regarded as expressing the fact that a concept falls under a higher one.* But this does not in any way efface the distinction between object and concept. We see to

* In my *Grundlagen* I called such a concept a second-order concept; in my work *Function und Begriff* I called it a second-level concept, as I shall do here.

begin with that in the sentence 'there is at least one square root of 4' the predicative nature of the concept is not belied; we could say 'there is something that has the property of giving the result 4 when multiplied by itself.' Hence what is here asserted about a concept can never be asserted about an object; for a proper name can never be a predicative expression, though it can be part of one. I do not want to say it is false to assert about an object what is asserted here about a concept; I want to say it is impossible, senseless, to do so. The sentence 'there is Julius Caesar' is neither true nor false but senseless; the sentence 'there is a man whose name is Julius Caesar' has a sense, but here again we have a concept, as the indefinite article shows. We get the same thing in the sentence 'there is only one Vienna.' We must not let ourselves be deceived because language often uses the same word now as a proper name, now as a concept-word; in our example, the numeral indicates that we have the latter; 'Vienna' is here a concept-word, like 'metropolis.' Using it in this sense, we may say: 'Trieste is no Vienna.' If, on the other hand, we substitute p. 201] 'Julius Caesar' for the proper name formed by the first six words of the sentence 'the concept *square root of 4* is realized,' we get a sentence that has a sense but is false; for the assertion that something is realized (as the word is being taken here) can be truly made only about a quite special kind of objects, viz. such as can be designated by proper names of the form 'the concept *F*.' Thus the words 'the concept *square root of 4*' have an essentially different behaviour, as regards possible substitutions, from the words 'square root of 4' in our original sentence; i.e. the reference of the two phrases is essentially different.

What has been shown here in one example holds good generally; the behaviour of the concept is essentially predicative, even where something is being asserted about it; consequently it can be replaced there only by another concept, never by an object. Thus the assertion that is made about a concept does not suit an object. Second-level concepts, which concepts fall under, are essentially different from first-level concepts, which objects fall under. The relation of an object to a first-level concept that it falls under is different from the (admittedly similar) relation of a first-level to a second-level concept. (To do justice at once

to the distinction and to the similarity, we might perhaps say:
An object falls *under* a first-level concept; a concept falls *within*
a second-level concept.) The distinction of concept and object
thus still holds, with all its sharpness.[A]

With this there hangs together what I have said (*Grundlagen*,
§ 53) about my usage of the words 'property' and 'mark'; Kerry's
discussion gives me occasion to revert once more to this. The
words serve to signify relations, in sentences like 'Φ is a property
of Γ' and 'Φ is a mark of Ω.' In my way of speaking, a thing can
be at once a property and a mark, but not of the same thing.
I call the concepts under which an object falls its properties; thus

'to be Φ is a property of Γ'

is just another way of saying:

'Γ falls under the concept of a Φ.'

If the object Γ has the properties Φ, X, and Ψ, I may combine
them into Ω; so that it is the same thing if I say that Γ has the
p. 202] property Ω, or, that Γ has the properties Φ, X, and Ψ. I
then call Φ, X, and Ψ marks of the concept Ω, and, at the same
time, properties of Γ. It is clear that the relations of Φ to Γ and
to Ω are quite different, and that consequently different terms are
required. Γ falls under the concept Φ; but Ω, which is itself a
concept, cannot fall under the first-level concept Φ; only to a
second-level concept could it stand in a similar relation. Ω is,
on the other hand, subordinate to Φ.

Let us consider an example. Instead of saying:

'2 is a positive number' and
'2 is a whole number' and
'2 is less than 10'

we may also say

'2 is a positive whole number less than 10.'

[A] When Russell says that expressions like 'the King of France' are not names but
incomplete symbols, he is saying what would be put thus in Frege's terminology: 'In
"the King of France is bald," "the King of France" is not a name of an object; what it
stands for is something incomplete, *ungesättigt*—a *second-level* concept, within which
the concept *bald* is falsely asserted to fall. This second-level concept is one *within* which
a concept falls if and only if there falls *under* it someone who is a King of France and apart
from whom nobody is a King of France; no first-level concept does fall within this,
because nobody is a King of France.'
It should, however, be emphasized that Frege himself gives an entirely different
account of definite descriptions. Cf. *Ueber Sinn und Bedeutung*, pp. 39–42.

Here

to be a positive number,
to be a whole number,
to be less than 10,

appear as properties of the object 2, and also as marks of the concept

positive whole number less than 10.

This is neither positive, nor a whole number, nor less than 10. It is indeed subordinate to the concept *whole number*, but does not fall under it.

Let us now compare with this what Kerry says in his second article (p. 224). 'By the number 4 we understand the result of additively combining 3 and 1. The concept object here occurring is the numerical individual 4; a quite definite number in the natural number-series. This object obviously bears just the marks that are named in its concept, and no others besides—provided we refrain, as we surely must, from counting as *propria* of the object its infinitely numerous relations to all other individual numbers; "the" number 4 is likewise the result of additively combining 3 and 1.'

We see at once that my distinction between property and mark is here quite slurred over. Kerry distinguishes here between the number 4 and 'the' number 4. I must confess that this distinction is incomprehensible to me. The number 4 is to be a concept; 'the' number 4 is to be a concept-object, and none other than the numerical individual 4. It needs no proof that what we have here p. 203] is not my distinction between concept and object. It almost looks as though what was floating (though very obscurely) before Kerry's mind were my distinction between the sense and the reference of the words 'the number 4.'* But it is only of the reference of the words that we can say: this is the result of additively combining 3 and 1.

Again, how are we to take the word 'is' in the sentences 'the number 4 is the result of additively combining 3 and 1' and ' "the" number 4 is the result of additively combining 3 and 1'? Is it a mere copula, or does it help to express a logical equation?

* Cf. my essay 'On Sense and Reference' (cited above).

In the first case, 'the' would have to be left out before 'result,' and the sentences would go like this:

'The number 4 is a result of additively combining 3 and 1';
' "The" number 4 is a result of additively combining 3 and 1.'

In that case, the objects that Kerry designates by

'the number 4' and ' "the" number 4'

would both fall under the concept

result of additively combining 3 and 1.

And then the only question would be what difference there was between these objects. (I am here using the words 'object' and 'concept' in my accustomed way.) I should express as follows what Kerry is apparently trying to say:

'The number 4 has those properties, and those alone, which are marks of the concept: *result of additively combining 3 and 1.*'

I should then express as follows the sense of the first of our two sentences:

'To be a number 4 is the same as being a result of additive combination of 3 and 1.'

In that case, what I conjectured just now to have been Kerry's intention could also be put thus:

'The number 4 has those properties, and those alone, which are marks of the concept *a number 4.*'

p. 204] (We need not here decide whether this is true.) The inverted commas around the definite article in the words ' "the" number 4' could in that case be omitted.

But in these attempted interpretations we have assumed that in at least one of the two sentences the definite articles in front of 'result' and 'number 4' were inserted only by an oversight. If we take the words as they stand, we can only regard them as having the sense of a logical equation, like:

'The number 4 is none other than the result of additively combining 3 and 1.'

The definite article in front of 'result' is here logically justified only if it is known (i) that there is such a result; (ii) that there is not more than one. In that case, the phrase designates an object, and is to be regarded as a proper name. If both of our sentences were to be regarded as logical equations, then, since their right sides are identical, it would follow from them that the number 4 is 'the' number 4, or, if you prefer, that the number 4 is no other than 'the' number 4; and so Kerry's distinction would have been proved untenable. However, it is not my present task to point out contradictions in his exposition; his way of taking the words 'object' and 'concept' is not properly my concern here. I am only trying to set my own usage of these words in a clearer light, and incidentally show that in any case it differs from his, whether that is consistent or not.

I do not at all dispute Kerry's right to use the words 'concept' and 'object' in his own way, if only he would respect my equal right, and admit that with my use of terms I have got hold of a distinction of the highest importance. I admit that there is a quite peculiar obstacle in the way of an understanding with my reader. By a kind of necessity of language, my expressions, taken literally, sometimes miss my thought; I mention an object, when what I intend is a concept. I fully realize that in such cases I was relying upon a reader who would be ready to meet me half-way—who does not begrudge a pinch of salt.

Somebody may think that this is an artificially created difficulty; that there is no need at all to take account of such an unmanageable thing as what I call a concept; that one might, like Kerry, regard an object's falling under a concept as a relation, in which the same thing could occur now as object, now as concept. p. 205] The words 'object' and 'concept' would then serve only to indicate the different positions in the relation. This may be done; but anybody who thinks the difficulty is avoided this way is very much mistaken; it is only shifted. For not all the parts of a thought can be complete; at least one must be 'unsaturated,' or predicative; otherwise they would not hold together. For example, the sense of the phrase 'the number 2' does not hold together with that of the expression 'the concept *prime number*' without a link. We apply such a link in the sentence 'the number 2 falls under the concept *prime number*'; it is contained in the words 'falls under,' which need to be completed in two ways—by a subject and an accusative; and only because their sense is thus 'unsaturated' are they capable of serving as a link. Only when they have been supplemented in this twofold respect do we get a complete sense, a thought. I say that such words or phrases stand for a relation. We now get the same difficulty for the relation that we were trying to avoid for the concept. For the words 'the relation of an object to the concept it falls under' designate not a relation but an object; and the three proper names 'the number 2,' 'the concept *prime number*,' 'the relation of an object to a concept it falls under,' hold aloof from one another just as much as the first two do by themselves; however we put them together, we get no sentence. It is thus easy for us to see that the difficulty arising from the 'unsaturatedness' of one part of the thought can indeed be shifted, but not avoided. 'Complete' and 'unsaturated' are of course only figures of speech; but all that I wish or am able to do here is to give hints.

It may make it easier to come to an understanding if the reader compares my work *Function und Begriff*. For over the question what it is that is called a function in Analysis, we come up against the same obstacle; and on thorough investigation it will be found that the obstacle is essential, and founded on the nature of our language; that we cannot avoid a certain inappropriateness of linguistic expression; and that there is nothing for it but to realize this and always take it into account.

ON SENSE AND REFERENCE

First published in *Zeitschrift für Philosophie und philosophische Kritik*, vol. 100 (1892), pp. 25–50

25] EQUALITY* gives rise to challenging questions which are not altogether easy to answer. Is it a relation? A relation between objects, or between names or signs of objects? In my *Begriffsschrift*ᴬ I assumed the latter. The reasons which seem to favour this are the following: $a=a$ and $a=b$ are obviously statements of differing cognitive value; $a=a$ holds *a priori* and, according to Kant, is to be labelled analytic, while statements of the form $a=b$ often contain very valuable extensions of our knowledge and cannot always be established *a priori*. The discovery that the rising sun is not new every morning, but always the same, was one of the most fertile astronomical discoveries. Even to-day the identification of a small planet or a comet is not always a 26] matter of course. Now if we were to regard equality as a relation between that which the names 'a' and 'b' designate, it would seem that $a=b$ could not differ from $a=a$ (i.e. provided $a=b$ is true). A relation would thereby be expressed of a thing to itself, and indeed one in which each thing stands to itself but to no other thing. What is intended to be said by $a=b$ seems to be that the signs or names 'a' and 'b' designate the same thing, so that those signs themselves would be under discussion; a relation between them would be asserted. But this relation would hold between the names or signs only in so far as they named or designated something. It would be mediated by the connexion of each of the two signs with

* I use this word in the sense of identity and understand '$a = b$' to have the sense of 'a is the same as b' or 'a and b coincide.'

ᴬ The reference is to Frege's *Begriffsschrift, eine der arithmetischen nachgebildete Formelsprache des reinen Denkens* (Halle, 1879).

the same designated thing. But this is arbitrary. Nobody can be forbidden to use any arbitrarily producible event or object as a sign for something. In that case the sentence $a=b$ would no longer refer to the subject matter, but only to its mode of designation; we would express no proper knowledge by its means. But in many cases this is just what we want to do. If the sign 'a' is distinguished from the sign 'b' only as object (here, by means of its shape), not as sign (i.e. not by the manner in which it designates something), the cognitive value of $a=a$ becomes essentially equal to that of $a=b$, provided $a=b$ is true. A difference can arise only if the difference between the signs corresponds to a difference in the mode of presentation of that which is designated. Let a, b, c be the lines connecting the vertices of a triangle with the midpoints of the opposite sides. The point of intersection of a and b is then the same as the point of intersection of b and c. So we have different designations for the same point, and these names ('point of intersection of a and b,' 'point of intersection of b and c') likewise indicate the mode of presentation; and hence the statement contains actual knowledge.

It is natural, now, to think of there being connected with a sign (name, combination of words, letter), besides that to which the sign refers, which may be called the reference of the sign, also what I should like to call the *sense* of the sign, wherein the mode of presentation is contained. In our example, accordingly, the 27] reference of the expressions 'the point of intersection of a and b' and 'the point of intersection of b and c' would be the same, but not their senses. The reference of 'evening star' would be the same as that of 'morning star,' but not the sense.

It is clear from the context that by 'sign' and 'name' I have here understood any designation representing a proper name, which thus has as its reference a definite object (this word taken in the widest range), but not a concept or a relation, which shall be discussed further in another article.[B] The designation of a single object can also consist of several words or other signs. For brevity, let every such designation be called a proper name.

The sense of a proper name is grasped by everybody who is sufficiently familiar with the language or totality of designations

---

[B] See his 'Ueber Begriff und Gegenstand' (*Vierteljahrsschrift für wissenschaftliche Philosophie* XVI [1892], 192–205).

to which it belongs;* but this serves to illuminate only a single aspect of the reference, supposing it to have one. Comprehensive knowledge of the reference would require us to be able to say immediately whether any given sense belongs to it. To such knowledge we never attain.

The regular connexion between a sign, its sense, and its reference is of such a kind that to the sign there corresponds a definite sense and to that in turn a definite reference, while to a given reference (an object) there does not belong only a single sign. The same sense has different expressions in different languages or even in the same language. To be sure, exceptions to this regular behaviour occur. To every expression belonging to a complete totality of signs, there should certainly correspond 28] a definite sense; but natural languages often do not satisfy this condition, and one must be content if the same word has the same sense in the same context. It may perhaps be granted that every grammatically well-formed expression representing a proper name always has a sense. But this is not to say that to the sense there also corresponds a reference. The words 'the celestial body most distant from the Earth' have a sense, but it is very doubtful if they also have a reference. The expression 'the least rapidly convergent series' has a sense but demonstrably has no reference, since for every given convergent series, another convergent, but less rapidly convergent, series can be found. In grasping a sense, one is not certainly assured of a reference.

If words are used in the ordinary way, what one intends to speak of is their reference. It can also happen, however, that one wishes to talk about the words themselves or their sense. This happens, for instance, when the words of another are quoted. One's own words then first designate words of the other speaker, and only the latter have their usual reference. We then have signs of signs. In writing, the words are in this case enclosed in quotation marks. Accordingly, a word standing between

* In the case of an actual proper name such as 'Aristotle' opinions as to the sense may differ. It might, for instance, be taken to be the following: the pupil of Plato and teacher of Alexander the Great. Anybody who does this will attach another sense to the sentence 'Aristotle was born in Stagira' than will a man who takes as the sense of the name: the teacher of Alexander the Great who was born in Stagira. So long as the reference remains the same, such variations of sense may be tolerated, although they are to be avoided in the theoretical structure of a demonstrative science and ought not to occur in a perfect language.

quotation marks must not be taken as having its ordinary reference.

In order to speak of the sense of an expression 'A' one may simply use the phrase 'the sense of the expression "A"'. In reported speech one talks about the sense, e.g., of another person's remarks. It is quite clear that in this way of speaking words do not have their customary reference but designate what is usually their sense. In order to have a short expression, we will say: In reported speech, words are used *indirectly* or have their *indirect* reference. We distinguish accordingly the *customary* from the *indirect* reference of a word; and its *customary* sense from its *indirect* sense. The indirect reference of a word is accordingly its customary sense. Such exceptions must always be borne in mind if the mode of connexion between sign, sense, and reference in particular cases is to be correctly understood.

29] The reference and sense of a sign are to be distinguished from the associated idea. If the reference of a sign is an object perceivable by the senses, my idea of it is an internal image,* arising from memories of sense impressions which I have had and acts, both internal and external, which I have performed. Such an idea is often saturated with feeling; the clarity of its separate parts varies and oscillates. The same sense is not always connected, even in the same man, with the same idea. The idea is subjective: one man's idea is not that of another. There result, as a matter of course, a variety of differences in the ideas associated with the same sense. A painter, a horseman, and a zoologist will probably connect different ideas with the name 'Bucephalus.' This constitutes an essential distinction between the idea and the sign's sense, which may be the common property of many and therefore is not a part or a mode of the individual mind. For one can hardly deny that mankind has a common store of thoughts which is transmitted from one generation to another.†

* We can include with ideas the direct experiences in which sense-impressions and acts themselves take the place of the traces which have left in the mind. The distinction is unimportant for our purpose, especially since memories of sense-impressions and acts always go along with such impressions and acts themselves to complete the perceptual image. One may on the other hand understand direct experience as including any object, in so far as it is sensibly perceptible or spatial.

† Hence it is inadvisable to use the word 'idea' to designate something so basically different.

In the light of this, one need have no scruples in speaking simply of *the* sense, whereas in the case of an idea one must, strictly speaking, add to whom it belongs and at what time. It might perhaps be said: Just as one man connects this idea, and another that idea, with the same word, so also one man can associate this sense and another that sense. But there still remains a difference in the mode of connexion. They are not prevented from grasping the same sense; but they cannot have the same 30] idea. *Si duo idem faciunt, non est idem.* If two persons picture the same thing, each still has his own idea. It is indeed sometimes possible to establish differences in the ideas, or even in the sensations, of different men; but an exact comparison is not possible, because we cannot have both ideas together in the same consciousness.

The reference of a proper name is the object itself which we designate by its means; the idea, which we have in that case, is wholly subjective; in between lies the sense, which is indeed no longer subjective like the idea, but is yet not the object itself. The following analogy will perhaps clarify these relationships. Somebody observes the Moon through a telescope. I compare the Moon itself to the reference; it is the object of the observation, mediated by the real image projected by the object glass in the interior of the telescope, and by the retinal image of the observer. The former I compare to the sense, the latter is like the idea or experience. The optical image in the telescope is indeed one-sided and dependent upon the standpoint of observation; but it is still objective, inasmuch as it can be used by several observers. At any rate it could be arranged for several to use it simultaneously. But each one would have his own retinal image. On account of the diverse shapes of the observers' eyes, even a geometrical congruence could hardly be achieved, and an actual coincidence would be out of the question. This analogy might be developed still further, by assuming A's retinal image made visible to B; or A might also see his own retinal image in a mirror. In this way we might perhaps show how an idea can itself be taken as an object, but as such is not for the observer what it directly is for the person having the idea. But to pursue this would take us too far afield.

We can now recognize three levels of difference between words, expressions, or whole sentences. The difference may concern at most the ideas, or the sense but not the reference, or, finally, the reference as well. With respect to the first level, it is to be 31] noted that, on account of the uncertain connexion of ideas with words, a difference may hold for one person, which another does not find. The difference between a translation and the original text should properly not overstep the first level. To the possible differences here belong also the colouring and shading which poetic eloquence seeks to give to the sense. Such colouring and shading are not objective, and must be evoked by each hearer or reader according to the hints of the poet or the speaker. Without some affinity in human ideas art would certainly be impossible; but it can never be exactly determined how far the intentions of the poet are realized.

In what follows there will be no further discussion of ideas and experiences; they have been mentioned here only to ensure that the idea aroused in the hearer by a word shall not be confused with its sense or its reference.

To make short and exact expressions possible, let the following phraseology be established:

A proper name (word, sign, sign combination, expression) *expresses* its sense, *stands for* or *designates* its reference. By means of a sign we express its sense and designate its reference.

Idealists or sceptics will perhaps long since have objected: 'You talk, without further ado, of the Moon as an object; but how do you know that the name 'the Moon' has any reference? How do you know that anything whatsoever has a reference?' I reply that when we say 'the Moon,' we do not intend to speak of our idea of the Moon, nor are we satisfied with the sense alone, but we presuppose a reference. To assume that in the sentence 'The Moon is smaller than the Earth' the idea of the Moon is in question, would be flatly to misunderstand the sense. If this is what the speaker wanted, he would use the phrase 'my idea of the Moon.' Now we can of course be mistaken in the presupposition, and such mistakes have indeed occurred. But the question whether the presupposition is perhaps always mistaken 32] need not be answered here; in order to justify mention of the reference of a sign it is enough, at first, to point out our intention in speaking or thinking. (We must then add the reservation: provided such reference exists.)

So far we have considered the sense and reference only of such expressions, words, or signs as we have called proper names. We now inquire concerning the sense and reference for an entire declarative sentence. Such a sentence contains a thought.* Is this thought, now, to be regarded as its sense or its reference? Let us assume for the time being that the sentence has reference. If we now replace one word of the sentence by another having the same reference, but a different sense, this can have no bearing upon the reference of the sentence. Yet we can see that in such a case the thought changes; since, e.g., the thought in the sentence 'The morning star is a body illuminated by the Sun' differs from that in the sentence 'The evening star is a body illuminated by the Sun.' Anybody who did not know that the evening star is the morning star might hold the one thought to be true, the other false. The thought, accordingly, cannot be the reference of the sentence, but must rather be considered as the sense. What is the position now with regard to the reference? Have we a right even to inquire about it? Is it possible that a sentence as a whole has only a sense, but no reference? At any rate, one might expect that such sentences occur, just as there are parts of sentences having sense but no reference. And sentences which contain proper names without reference will be of this kind. The sentence 'Odysseus was set ashore at Ithaca while sound asleep' obviously has a sense. But since it is doubtful whether the name 'Odysseus,' occurring therein, has reference, it is also doubtful whether the whole sentence has one. Yet it is certain, nevertheless, that anyone who seriously took the sentence to be true or false would ascribe to the name 'Odysseus' a reference, not merely 33] a sense; for it is of the reference of the name that the predicate is affirmed or denied. Whoever does not admit the name has reference can neither apply nor withhold the predicate. But in that case it would be superfluous to advance to the reference of the name; one could be satisfied with the sense, if one wanted to go no further than the thought. If it were a question only of the sense of the sentence, the thought, it would be

---

* By a thought I understand not the subjective performance of thinking but its objective content, which is capable of being the common property of several thinkers.

unnecessary to bother with the reference of a part of the sentence; only the sense, not the reference, of the part is relevant to the sense of the whole sentence. The thought remains the same whether 'Odysseus' has reference or not. The fact that we concern ourselves at all about the reference of a part of the sentence indicates that we generally recognize and expect a reference for the sentence itself. The thought loses value for us as soon as we recognize that the reference of one of its parts is missing. We are therefore justified in not being satisfied with the sense of a sentence, and in inquiring also as to its reference. But now why do we want every proper name to have not only a sense, but also a reference? Why is the thought not enough for us? Because, and to the extent that, we are concerned with its truth value. This is not always the case. In hearing an epic poem, for instance, apart from the euphony of the language we are interested only in the sense of the sentences and the images and feelings thereby aroused. The question of truth would cause us to abandon aesthetic delight for an attitude of scientific investigation. Hence it is a matter of no concern to us whether the name 'Odysseus,' for instance, has reference, so long as we accept the poem as a work of art.* It is the striving for truth that drives us always to advance from the sense to the reference.

We have seen that the reference of a sentence may always be sought, whenever the reference of its components is involved; and that this is the case when and only when we are inquiring after the truth value.

34] We are therefore driven into accepting the *truth value* of a sentence as constituting its reference. By the truth value of a sentence I understand the circumstance that it is true or false. There are no further truth values. For brevity I call the one the True, the other the False. Every declarative sentence concerned with the reference of its words is therefore to be regarded as a proper name, and its reference, if it has one, is either the True or the False. These two objects are recognized, if only implicitly, by everybody who judges something to be true—and so even by a sceptic. The designation of the truth values as objects may

* It would be desirable to have a special term for signs having only sense. If we name them, say, representations, the words of the actors on the stage would be representations; indeed the actor himself would be a representation.

appear to be an arbitrary fancy or perhaps a mere play upon words, from which no profound consequences could be drawn. What I mean by an object can be more exactly discussed only in connexion with concept and relation. I will reserve this for another article.[c] But so much should already be clear, that in every judgment,[*] no matter how trivial, the step from the level of thoughts to the level of reference (the objective) has already been taken.

One might be tempted to regard the relation of the thought to the True not as that of sense to reference, but rather as that of subject to predicate. One can, indeed, say: 'The thought, that 5 is a prime number, is true.' But closer examination shows that nothing more has been said than in the simple sentence '5 is a prime number.' The truth claim arises in each case from the form of the declarative sentence, and when the latter lacks its usual force, e.g., in the mouth of an actor upon the stage, even the sentence 'The thought that 5 is a prime number is true' contains only a thought, and indeed the same thought as the simple '5 is a prime number.' It follows that the relation of the thought to the True may not be compared with that of subject to predicate. 35] Subject and predicate (understood in the logical sense) are indeed elements of thought; they stand on the same level for knowledge. By combining subject and predicate, one reaches only a thought, never passes from sense to reference, never from a thought to its truth value. One moves at the same level but never advances from one level to the next. A truth value cannot be a part of a thought, any more than, say, the Sun can, for it is not a sense but an object.

If our supposition that the reference of a sentence is its truth value is correct, the latter must remain unchanged when a part of the sentence is replaced by an expression having the same reference. And this is in fact the case. Leibniz gives the definition: 'Eadem sunt, quae sibi mutuo substitui possunt, salva veritate.' What else but the truth value could be found, that belongs quite generally to every sentence if the reference of its components is relevant, and remains unchanged by substitutions of the kind in question?

c See his 'Ueber Begriff und Gegenstand' (Vierteljahrsschrift für wissenschaftliche Philosophie XVI [1892], 192–205).

* A judgment, for me is not the mere comprehension of a thought, but the admission of its truth.

If now the truth value of a sentence is its reference, then on the one hand all true sentences have the same reference and so, on the other hand, do all false sentences. From this we see that in the reference of the sentence all that is specific is obliterated. We can never be concerned only with the reference of a sentence; but again the mere thought alone yields no knowledge, but only the thought together with its reference, i.e. its truth value. Judgments can be regarded as advances from a thought to a truth value. Naturally this cannot be a definition. Judgment is something quite peculiar and incomparable. One might also say that judgments are distinctions of parts within truth values. Such distinction occurs by a return to the thought. To every sense belonging to a truth value there would correspond its own manner of analysis. However, I have here used the word 'part' in a special sense. I have in fact transferred the relation between the parts and the whole of the sentence to its reference, by calling the reference of a word part of the reference of the sentence, if the 36] word itself is a part of the sentence. This way of speaking can certainly be attacked, because the whole reference and one part of it do not suffice to determine the remainder, and because the word 'part' is already used in another sense of bodies. A special term would need to be invented.

The supposition that the truth value of a sentence is its reference shall now be put to further test. We have found that the truth value of a sentence remains unchanged when an expression is replaced by another having the same reference: but we have not yet considered the case in which the expression to be replaced is itself a sentence. Now if our view is correct, the truth value of a sentence containing another as part must remain unchanged when the part is replaced by another sentence having the same truth value. Exceptions are to be expected when the whole sentence or its part is direct or indirect quotation; for in such cases, as we have seen, the words do not have their customary reference. In direct quotation, a sentence designates another sentence, and in indirect quotation a thought.

We are thus led to consider subordinate sentences or clauses. These occur as parts of a sentence complex, which is, from the logical standpoint, likewise a sentence—a main sentence. But here we meet the question whether it is also true of the subordinate sentence that its reference is a truth value. Of indirect quotation we already know the opposite. Grammarians view subordinate clauses as representatives of parts of sentences and divide them accordingly into noun clauses, adjective clauses, adverbial clauses. This might generate the supposition that the reference of a subordinate clause was not a truth value but rather of the same kind as the reference of a noun or adjective or adverb—in short, of a part of a sentence, whose sense was not a thought but only a part of a thought. Only a more thorough investigation can clarify the issue. In so doing, we shall not follow the grammatical categories strictly, but rather group together what is logically of the same kind. Let us first search for cases in which the sense of the subordinate clause, as we have just supposed, is not an independent thought.

37] The case of an abstract[D] noun clause, introduced by 'that,' includes the case of indirect quotation, in which we have seen the words to have their indirect reference coinciding with what is customarily their sense. In this case, then, the subordinate clause has for its reference a thought, not a truth value; as sense not a thought, but the sense of the words 'the thought, that . . .,' which is only a part of the thought in the entire complex sentence. This happens after 'say,' 'hear,' 'be of the opinion,' 'be convinced,' 'conclude,' and similar words.* There is a different, and indeed somewhat complicated, situation after words like 'perceive,' 'know,' 'fancy,' which are to be considered later.

That in the cases of the first kind the reference of the subordinate clause is in fact the thought can also be recognized by seeing that it is indifferent to the truth of the whole whether the subordinate clause is true or false. Let us compare, for instance, the two sentences 'Copernicus believed that the planetary orbits are circles' and 'Copernicus believed that the apparent motion of the sun is produced by the real motion of the Earth.' One subordinate clause can be substituted for the other without harm to the truth. The main clause and the subordinate clause together have as their sense only a single thought, and the truth of the whole includes neither the truth nor the untruth of the subordinate clause.

D A literal translation of Frege's 'abstracten Nennsätzen' whose meaning eludes me.

* In 'A lied in saying he had seen B,' the subordinate clause designates a thought which is said (1) to have been asserted by A (2) while A was convinced of its falsity.

In such cases it is not permissible to replace one expression in the subordinate clause by another having the same customary reference, but only by one having the same indirect reference, i.e. the same customary sense. If somebody were to conclude: The reference of a sentence is not its truth value, for in that case it could always be replaced by another sentence of the same truth value; he would prove too much; one might just as well claim that the reference of 'morning star' is not Venus, since one may not always say 'Venus' in place of 'morning star.' One has the right to conclude only that the reference of a sentence is not *always* its truth value, and that 'morning star' does not always 38] stand for the planet Venus, viz. when the word has its indirect reference. An exception of such a kind occurs in the subordinate clause just considered which has a thought as its reference.

If one says 'It seems that . . .' one means 'It seems to me that . . .' or 'I think that . . .' We therefore have the same case again. The situation is similar in the case of expressions such as 'to be pleased,' 'to regret,' 'to approve,' 'to blame,' 'to hope,' 'to fear.' If, toward the end of the battle of Waterloo,[E] Wellington was glad that the Prussians were coming, the basis for his joy was a conviction. Had he been deceived, he would have been no less pleased so long as his illusion lasted; and before he became so convinced he could not have been pleased that the Prussians were coming—even though in fact they might have been already approaching.

Just as a conviction or a belief is the ground of a feeling, it can, as in inference, also be the ground of a conviction. In the sentence: 'Columbus inferred from the roundness of the Earth that he could reach India by travelling towards the west,' we have as the reference of the parts two thoughts, that the Earth is round, and that Columbus by travelling to the west could reach India. All that is relevant here is that Columbus was convinced of both, and that the one conviction was a ground for the other. Whether the Earth is really round and Columbus could really reach India by travelling west, as he thought, is immaterial to the truth of our sentence; but it is not immaterial whether we replace 'the Earth' by 'the planet which is accompanied by a

---

E Frege uses the Prussian name for the battle—'Belle Alliance.'

moon whose diameter is greater than the fourth part of its own.'
Here also we have the indirect reference of the words.

Adverbial final clauses beginning 'in order that' also belong
here; for obviously the purpose is a thought; therefore: indirect
reference for the words, subjunctive mood.

A subordinate clause with 'that' after 'command,' 'ask,' 'forbid,' would appear in direct speech as an imperative. Such a
clause has no reference but only a sense. A command, a request,
are indeed not thoughts, yet they stand on the same level as
thoughts. Hence in subordinate clauses depending upon
39] 'command,' 'ask,' etc., words have their indirect reference.
The reference of such a clause is therefore not a truth value but a
command, a request, and so forth.

The case is similar for the dependent question in phrases such
as 'doubt whether,' 'not to know what.' It is easy to see that here
also the words are to be taken to have their indirect reference.
Dependent clauses expressing questions and beginning with
'who,' 'what,' 'where,' 'when,' 'how,' 'by what means,' etc.,
seem at times to approximate very closely to adverbial clauses in
which words have their customary references. These cases are
distinguished linguistically [in German] by the mood of the verb.
With the subjunctive, we have a dependent question and indirect
reference of the words, so that a proper name cannot in general
be replaced by another name of the same object.

In the cases so far considered the words of the subordinate
clauses had their indirect reference, and this made it clear that the
reference of the subordinate clause itself was indirect, i.e. not a
truth value but a thought, a command, a request, a question.
The subordinate clause could be regarded as a noun, indeed one
could say: as a proper name of that thought, that command, etc.,
which it represented in the context of the sentence structure.

We now come to other subordinate clauses, in which the words
do have their customary reference without however a thought
occurring as sense and a truth value as reference. How this is
possible is best made clear by examples.

Whoever discovered the elliptic form of the planetary orbits died in misery.

If the sense of the subordinate clause were here a thought, it
would have to be possible to express it also in a separate sentence.

But this does not work, because the grammatical subject 'whoever' has no independent sense and only mediates the relation with the consequent clause 'died in misery.' For this reason the sense of the subordinate clause is not a complete thought, and its reference is Kepler, not a truth value. One might object that the sense of the whole does contain a thought as part, viz. that there was somebody who first discovered the elliptic form of the planetary orbits; for whoever takes the whole to be true cannot 40] deny this part. This is undoubtedly so; but only because otherwise the dependent clause 'whoever discovered the elliptic form of the planetary orbits' would have no reference. If anything is asserted there is always an obvious presupposition that the simple or compound proper names used have reference. If one therefore asserts 'Kepler died in misery,' there is a presupposition that the name 'Kepler' designates something; but it does not follow that the sense of the sentence 'Kepler died in misery' contains the thought that the name 'Kepler' designates something. If this were the case the negation would have to run not

Kepler did not die in misery

but

Kepler did not die in misery, or the name 'Kepler' has no reference.

That the name 'Kepler' designates something is just as much a presupposition for the assertion

Kepler died in misery

as for the contrary assertion. Now languages have the fault of containing expressions which fail to designate an object (although their grammatical form seems to qualify them for that purpose) because the truth of some sentence is a prerequisite. Thus it depends on the truth of the sentence:

There was someone who discovered the elliptic form of the planetary orbits

whether the subordinate clause

Whoever discovered the elliptic form of the planetary orbits

really designates an object or only seems to do so while having in fact no reference. And thus it may appear as if our subordinate clause contained as a part of its sense the thought that there was somebody who discovered the elliptic form of the planetary orbits. If this were right the negation would run:

> Either whoever discovered the elliptic form of the planetary orbits did not die in misery or there was nobody who discovered the elliptic form of the planetary orbits.

41] This arises from an imperfection of language, from which even the symbolic language of mathematical analysis is not altogether free; even there combinations of symbols can occur that seem to stand for something but have (at least so far) no reference, e.g. divergent infinite series. This can be avoided, e.g., by means of the special stipulation that divergent infinite series shall stand for the number 0. A logically perfect language (*Begriffsschrift*) should satisfy the conditions, that every expression grammatically well constructed as a proper name out of signs already introduced shall in fact designate an object, and that no new sign shall be introduced as a proper name without being secured a reference. The logic books contain warnings against logical mistakes arising from the ambiguity of expressions. I regard as no less pertinent a warning against apparent proper names having no reference. The history of mathematics supplies errors which have arisen in this way. This lends itself to demagogic abuse as easily as ambiguity—perhaps more easily. 'The will of the people' can serve as an example; for it is easy to establish that there is at any rate no generally accepted reference for this expression. It is therefore by no means unimportant to eliminate the source of these mistakes, at least in science, once and for all. Then such objections as the one discussed above would become impossible, because it could never depend upon the truth of a thought whether a proper name had a reference.

With the consideration of these noun clauses may be coupled that of types of adjective and adverbial clauses which are logically in close relation to them.

Adjective clauses also serve to construct compound proper names, though, unlike noun clauses, they are not sufficient by themselves for this purpose. These adjective clauses are to be regarded as equivalent to adjectives. Instead of 'the square root of 4 which is smaller than 0,' one can also say 'the negative square root of 4.' We have here the case of a compound proper name constructed from the expression for a concept with the help of the

singular definite article. This is at any rate permissible if the
42] concept applies to one and only one single object.*

Expressions for concepts can be so constructed that marks of a
concept are given by adjective clauses as, in our example, by the
clause 'which is smaller than o.' It is evident that such an adjective
clause cannot have a thought as sense or a truth value as reference,
any more than the noun clause could. Its sense, which can also
be expressed in many cases by a single adjective, is only a part of a
thought. Here, as in the case of the noun clause, there is no
independent subject and therefore no possibility of reproducing
the sense of the subordinate clause in an independent sentence.

Places, instants, stretches of time, are, logically considered,
objects; hence the linguistic designation of a definite place, a
definite instant, or a stretch of time is to be regarded as a proper
name. Now adverbial clauses of place and time can be used for
the construction of such a proper name in a manner similar to
that which we have seen in the case of noun and adjective clauses.
In the same way, expressions for concepts bringing in places,
etc., can be constructed. It is to be noted here also that the
sense of these subordinate clauses cannot be reproduced in an
independent sentence, since an essential component, viz. the
determination of place or time, is missing and is only indicated
by a relative pronoun or a conjunction.†

In conditional clauses, also, there may usually be recognized to

---

* In accordance with what was said above, an expression of the kind in question must
actually always be assured of reference, by means of a special stipulation, e.g. by the
convention that 0 shall count as its reference, when the concept applies to no object or
to more than one.

† In the case of these sentences, various interpretations are easily possible. The sense
of the sentence, 'After Schleswig-Holstein was separated from Denmark, Prussia and
Austria quarrelled' can also be rendered in the form 'After the separation of Schleswig-
Holstein from Denmark, Prussia and Austria quarrelled.' In this version, it is surely sufficiently clear that the sense is not to be taken as having as a part the thought that Schleswig-
Holstein was once separated from Denmark, but that this is the necessary presupposition
in order for the expression 'after the separation of Schleswig-Holstein from Denmark' to
have any reference at all. To be sure, our sentence can also be interpreted as saying that
Schleswig-Holstein was once separated from Denmark. We then have a case which is to
be considered later. In order to understand the difference more clearly, let us project
ourselves into the mind of a Chinese who, having little knowledge of European history,
believes it to be false that Schleswig-Holstein was ever separated from Denmark. He will
take our sentence, in the first version, to be neither true nor false but will deny it to have
any reference, on the ground of absence of reference for its subordinate clause. This clause
would only apparently determine a time. If he interpreted our sentence in the second way,
however, he would find a thought expressed in it which he would take to be false, beside
a part which would be without reference for him.

43] occur an indefinite indicator, having a similar correlate in the dependent clause. (We have already seen this occur in noun, adjective, and adverbial clauses.) In so far as each indicator refers to the other, both clauses together form a connected whole, which as a rule expresses only a single thought. In the sentence

If a number is less than 1 and greater than 0, its square is less than 1 and greater than 0

the component in question is 'a number' in the conditional clause and 'its' in the dependent clause. It is by means of this very indefiniteness that the sense acquires the generality expected of a law. It is this which is responsible for the fact that the antecedent clause alone has no complete thought as its sense and in combination with the consequent clause expresses one and only one thought, whose parts are no longer thoughts. It is, in general, incorrect to say that in the hypothetical judgment two judgments are put in reciprocal relationship. If this or something similar is said, the word 'judgment' is used in the same sense as I have connected with the word 'thought,' so that I would use the formulation: 'A hypothetical thought establishes a reciprocal relationship between two thoughts.' This could be true only if an indefinite indicator is absent;* but in such a case there would also be no generality.

If an instant of time is to be indefinitely indicated in both conditional and dependent clauses, this is often achieved merely by using the present tense of the verb, which in such a case however does not indicate the temporal present. This grammatical form is then the indefinite indicator in the main and 44] subordinate clauses. An example of this is: 'When the Sun is in the tropic of Cancer, the longest day in the northern hemisphere occurs.' Here, also, it is impossible to express the sense of the subordinate clause in a full sentence, because this sense is not a complete thought. If we say: 'The Sun is in the tropic of Cancer,' this would refer to our present time and thereby change the sense. Just as little is the sense of the main clause a thought; only the whole, composed of main and subordinate clauses, has such a sense. It may be added that several common components in the antecedent and consequent clauses may be indefinitely indicated.

* At times an explicit linguistic indication is missing and must be read off from the entire context.

It is clear that noun clauses with 'who' or 'what' and adverbial clauses with 'where,' 'when,' 'wherever,' 'whenever' are often to be interpreted as having the sense of conditional clauses, e.g. 'who touches pitch, defiles himself.'

Adjective clauses can also take the place of conditional clauses. Thus the sense of the sentence previously used can be given in the form 'The square of a number which is less than 1 and greater than 0 is less than 1 and greater than 0.'

The situation is quite different if the common component of the two clauses is designated by a proper name. In the sentence:

Napoleon, who recognized the danger to his right flank, himself led his guards against the enemy position

two thoughts are expressed:

1. Napoleon recognized the danger to his right flank
2. Napoleon himself led his guards against the enemy position.

When and where this happened is to be fixed only by the context, but is nevertheless to be taken as definitely determined thereby. If the entire sentence is uttered as an assertion, we thereby simultaneously assert both component sentences. If one of the parts is false, the whole is false. Here we have the case that the subordinate clause by itself has a complete thought as sense (if we complete it by indication of place and time). The reference of the subordinate clause is accordingly a truth value. We can therefore expect that it may be replaced, without harm to the truth value of the whole, by a sentence having the same truth 45] value. This is indeed the case; but it is to be noticed that for purely grammatical reasons, its subject must be 'Napoleon,' for only then can it be brought into the form of an adjective clause belonging to 'Napoleon.' But if the demand that it be expressed in this form be waived, and the connexion be shown by 'and,' this restriction disappears.

Subsidiary clauses beginning with 'although' also express complete thoughts. This conjunction actually has no sense and does not change the sense of the clause but only illuminates it in a peculiar fashion.* We could indeed replace the concessive clause without harm to the truth of the whole by another of the same truth value; but the light in which the clause is placed by the

* Similarly in the case of 'but,' 'yet.'

conjunction might then easily appear unsuitable, as if a song with a sad subject were to be sung in a lively fashion.

In the last cases the truth of the whole included the truth of the component clauses. The case is different if a conditional clause expresses a complete thought by containing, in place of an indefinite indicator, a proper name or something which is to be regarded as equivalent. In the sentence

If the Sun has already risen, the sky is very cloudy

the time is the present, that is to say, definite. And the place is also to be thought of as definite. Here it can be said that a relation between the truth values of conditional and dependent clauses has been asserted, viz. such that the case does not occur in which the antecedent stands for the True and the consequent for the False. Accordingly, our sentence is true if the Sun has not yet risen, whether the sky is very cloudy or not, and also if the Sun has risen and the sky is very cloudy. Since only truth values are here in question, each component clause can be replaced by another of the same truth value without changing the truth value of the whole. To be sure, the light in which the subject then appears would usually be unsuitable; the thought 46] might easily seem distorted; but this has nothing to do with its truth value. One must always take care not to clash with the subsidiary thoughts, which are however not explicitly expressed and therefore should not be reckoned in the sense. Hence, also, no account need be taken of their truth values.*

The simple cases have now been discussed. Let us review what we have learned.

The subordinate clause usually has for its sense not a thought, but only a part of one, and consequently no truth value as reference. The reason for this is either that the words in the subordinate clause have indirect reference, so that the reference, not the sense, of the subordinate clause is a thought; or else that, on account of the presence of an indefinite indicator, the subordinate clause is incomplete and expresses a thought only when combined with the main clause. It may happen, however, that the sense of the subsidiary clause is a complete thought, in

* The thought of our sentence might also be expressed thus: 'Either the Sun has not risen yet or the sky is very cloudy'—which shows how this kind of sentence connexion is to be understood.

which case it can be replaced by another of the same truth value without harm to the truth of the whole—provided there are no grammatical obstacles.

An examination of all the subordinate clauses which one may encounter will soon provide some which do not fit well into these categories. The reason, so far as I can see, is that these subordinate clauses have no such simple sense. Almost always, it seems, we connect with the main thoughts expressed by us subsidiary thoughts which, although not expressed, are associated with our words, in accordance with psychological laws, by the hearer. And since the subsidiary thought appears to be connected with our words of its own accord, almost like the main thought itself, we want it also to be expressed. The sense of the sentence is thereby enriched, and it may well happen that we have more simple thoughts than clauses. In many cases the sentence must be understood in this way, in others it may be doubtful whether the subsidiary thought belongs to the sense of the sentence or only 47] accompanies it.* One might perhaps find that the sentence

Napoleon, who recognized the danger to his right flank, himself led his guards against the enemy position

expresses not only the two thoughts shown above, but also the thought that the knowledge of the danger was the reason why he led the guards against the enemy position. One may in fact doubt whether this thought is merely slightly suggested or really expressed. Let the question be considered whether our sentence be false if Napoleon's decision had already been made before he recognized the danger. If our sentence could be true in spite of this, the subsidiary thought should not be understood as part of the sense. One would probably decide in favour of this. The alternative would make for a quite complicated situation: We would have more simple thoughts than clauses. If the sentence

Napoleon recognized the danger to his right flank

were now to be replaced by another having the same truth value, e.g.

Napoleon was already more than 45 years old

not only would our first thought be changed, but also our third

* This may be important for the question whether an assertion is a lie, or an oath a perjury.

one. Hence the truth value of the latter might change—viz. if his age was not the reason for the decision to lead the guards against the enemy. This shows why clauses of equal truth value cannot always be substituted for one another in such cases. The clause expresses more through its connexion with another than it does in isolation.

Let us now consider cases where this regularly happens. In the sentence:

> Bebel fancies that the return of Alsace-Lorraine would appease France's desire for revenge

two thoughts are expressed, which are not however shown by means of antecedent and consequent clauses, viz.:

> (1) Bebel believes that the return of Alsace-Lorraine would appease France's[f] desire for revenge
> 48] (2) the return of Alsace-Lorraine would not appease France's desire for revenge.

In the expression of the first thought, the words of the subordinate clause have their indirect reference, while the same words have their customary reference in the expression of the second thought. This shows that the subordinate clause in our original complex sentence is to be taken twice over, with different reference, standing once for a thought, once for a truth value. Since the truth value is not the whole reference of the subordinate clause, we cannot simply replace the latter by another of equal truth value. Similar considerations apply to expressions such as 'know,' 'discover,' 'it is known that.'

By means of a subordinate causal clause and the associated main clause we express several thoughts, which however do not correspond separately to the original clauses. In the sentence: 'Because ice is less dense than water, it floats on water' we have

> (1) Ice is less dense than water;
> (2) If anything is less dense than water, it floats on water;
> (3) Ice floats on water.

The third thought, however, need not be explicitly introduced, since it is contained in the remaining two. On the other hand, neither the first and third nor the second and third combined would furnish the sense of our sentence. It can now be seen that our subordinate clause

> because ice is less dense than water

expresses our first thought, as well as a part of our second. This is how it comes to pass that our subsidiary clause cannot be simply replaced by another of equal truth value; for this would alter our second thought and thereby might well alter its truth value.

The situation is similar in the sentence

> If iron were less dense than water, it would float on water.

49] Here we have the two thoughts that iron is not less dense than water, and that something floats on water if it is less dense than water. The subsidiary clause again expresses one thought and a part of the other.

If we interpret the sentence already considered

> After Schleswig-Holstein was separated from Denmark, Prussia and Austria quarrelled

in such a way that it expresses the thought that Schleswig-Holstein was once separated from Denmark, we have first this thought, and secondly the thought that at a time, more closely determined by the subordinate clause, Prussia and Austria quarrelled. Here also the subordinate clause expresses not only one thought but also a part of another. Therefore it may not in general be replaced by another of the same truth value.

It is hard to exhaust all the possibilities given by language; but I hope to have brought to light at least the essential reasons why a subordinate clause may not always be replaced by another of equal truth value without harm to the truth of the whole sentence structure. These reasons arise:

(1) when the subordinate clause does not stand for a truth value, inasmuch as it expresses only a part of a thought;

(2) when the subordinate clause does stand for a truth value but is not restricted to so doing, inasmuch as its sense includes one thought and part of another.

The first case arises:

(a) in indirect reference of words

(b) if a part of the sentence is only an indefinite indicator instead of a proper name.

In the second case, the subsidiary clause may have to be taken twice over, viz. once in its customary reference, and the other time in indirect reference; or the sense of a part of the subordinate clause may likewise be a component of another thought, which, taken together with the thought directly expressed by the subordinate clause, makes up the sense of the whole sentence.

It follows with sufficient probability from the foregoing that the cases where a subordinate clause is not replaceable by another of the same value cannot be brought in disproof of our view 50] that a truth value is the reference of a sentence having a thought as its sense.

Let us return to our starting point.

When we found '$a=a$' and '$a=b$' to have different cognitive values, the explanation is that for the purpose of knowledge, the sense of the sentence, viz., the thought expressed by it, is no less relevant than its reference, i.e. its truth value. If now $a=b$, then indeed the reference of 'b' is the same as that of 'a,' and hence the truth value of '$a=b$' is the same as that of '$a=a$.' In spite of this, the sense of 'b' may differ from that of 'a', and thereby the thought expressed in '$a=b$' differs from that of '$a=a$.' In that case the two sentences do not have the same cognitive value. If we understand by 'judgment' the advance from the thought to its truth value, as in the above paper, we can also say that the judgments are different.

Illustrative extracts from Frege's review of Husserl's *Philosophie der Arithmetik* (C. E. M. Pfeffer, Leipzig 1891) in *Zeitschrift für Philosophie und phil. Kritik*, vol. 103 (1894), pp. 313–332.

I. *On Imagination and Thought*

p. 317] . . . Thus we have a blurring of the distinction between image and concept, between imagination and thought. Everything is transformed into something subjective. But just because the boundary between the subjective and the objective is obliterated, what is subjective acquires in its turn the appearance of objectivity. People speak, e.g., of such-and-such a mental image, as if it could be in public view, detached from the imagining mind. And yet a man never has somebody else's mental image, but only his own; and nobody even knows how far his image (say) of red agrees with somebody else's; for the peculiar character of the image I connect with the word 'red' is something that I cannot convey. In order to be able to compare one man's mental images with another's, we should have to have united them into one and the same state of consciousness, and to be sure that they had not altered in the process of transference. It is quite otherwise p. 318] for thoughts; one and the same thought can be grasped by many men. The constituents of the thought, and *a fortiori* things themselves, must be distinguished from the images that accompany in some mind the act of grasping the thought—images that each man forms of things.

II. *On Definitions*

p. 318] . . . it is easy to understand the author's way of judging the value of definitions. An example from elementary geometry may illustrate it. The usual definition given there is: 'A right angle is an angle equal to its adjacent angle.' The author would probably comment on this as follows: 'The idea (*Vorstellung*) of a right angle is a simple one; so it is a wholly mistaken procedure to try to define it. Relation to another, adjacent, angle is in no way involved in our idea of a right angle. It is indeed correct to say:

The concepts "right angle" and "angle equal to its adjacent angle" have the same extension; but it is not correct to say they have the same content. The extension is being defined, in place of the content. If the definition were correct, any assertion that something is a right angle would refer, not to the concrete pair of sides we have before us, but only to their relation to another pair. All that we can admit is that equality with the adjacent angle gives us a necessary and sufficient criterion for a right angle.' (Cf. his p. 114.) It is in a similar way that the author (p. 115) judges the value of defining 'like-numbered' in terms of one-p. 319] one correlation. 'The simplest criterion for equality of number is just that *the same* number results from our counting the sets to be compared.' Naturally; just as the simplest test for a right angle is to apply a set square! The author forgets that this very counting depends on a one-one correlation—namely, between the numerals from 1 up to *n* and the objects in the set. Each of the two sets has to be counted. This makes the matter less simple than it is if we consider a relation that correlates the two sets without the numerals as intermediaries.

p. 320] . . . The objection that it is not the concept but its extension that is defined really touches all mathematical definitions. For the mathematician, it is no more right and no more wrong to define a conic section as the line of intersection of a plane with the surface of a circular cone than to define it as a plane curve with an equation of the second degree in Cartesian co-ordinates. Which definition he chooses—one of these two, or some other again—depends entirely on reasons of convenience; although these expressions neither have the same sense, nor evoke the same images. I do not mean by this that a concept and its extension are one and the same; but coincidence in extension is a necessary and sufficient criterion for the occurrence between concepts of the relation corresponding to identity between objects.* . . . I agree with the author that Leibniz's explanation *'eadem sunt quorum unum potest substitui alteri salva veritate'* does not deserve to be called a definition; my reasons, however, are different. Since any definition is an identity, identity itself cannot be defined. This explanation of Leibniz's could be called

* Identity, properly speaking, does not apply to concepts. Cf. my essay *On Concept and Object* in the *Zeitschrift für wiss. Philosophie.*

an axiom that brings out the nature of the relation of identity; as such, it is fundamentally important.[A]

III. *On Numerical Statements*

p. 321] According to the author, a numerical statement relates to the collective (set, plurality) of counted objects (p. 185). Such a collective can be expressed quite adequately by means of the conjunction 'and'. So we should expect that all numerical statements were of the form 'A and B and C and . . . and Q is *n*' or at least could be reduced to this form. But what do we really learn from the sentence 'Berlin and Dresden and Munich are three'; or, what is supposed to be the same, 'Berlin and Dresden and Munich are something and something and something'? Who would take the trouble to ask a question in order to get such an answer? It is not even meant that Berlin is different from Dresden, Dresden from Munich, and Munich from Berlin; indeed, the second form involves neither the distinctness of Berlin and Dresden nor their identity.[A] Now it is curious that in everyday life this form of numerical predication hardly ever occurs, and when it does occur it is not intended as a statement of number. I find that it is really used only in two cases: first, with the numeral 'two,' to express difference (*'Rübsen und Raps sind zwei'*—'rape-seed and rape are two (different things)'); secondly, with the numeral 'one,' to express identity[A]—'I and the Father are one.' The second example is specially fatal; for on the author's view it would have to run 'are something and something' or 'are two'! In fact we do not ask 'How many are Caesar and Pompey and London and Edinburgh?' or 'How many is Great Britain and Ireland?'; and I am curious to know how the author would answer. We do ask on the other hand, e.g., 'How many moons has Mars?' or 'What is the number of Martian moons?' and from the answer 'The number of Martian moons is two' we learn something worth asking about. So we see that both in the question and in the answer we get a word, or a complex designation, for a p. 322] concept, instead of the 'and' required by the author. How does he extricate himself from the difficulty? He says the number applies to the extension of the concept, the collective. 'It is only

[A] Here it seems best to render *Gleichheit* by 'identity' rather than 'equality.'

indirectly that one can say that the concept has the property of having an extension to which the number . . . applies.' (p. 189.) This really concedes all that I am maintaining: in the numerical statement, something is being asserted about a concept. I shall not dispute whether the assertion relates directly to the concept and indirectly to its extension, or indirectly to the concept and directly to the extension; for one goes with the other. But what is certain is that there is no direct designation either of an extension or of a collective, but only of a concept. If the author were using 'extension' in the same sense as I, we should hardly differ in opinion as to the sense of numerical assertions. This of course is not the case; for the extension of a concept is not a collective in the author's sense. A concept under which just one object falls has a definite extension; so has a concept under which no object falls; so has a concept under which infinitely many objects fall; and in all these cases, according to Husserl, there is no collective at all. The sense of the words 'extension of the concept *Martian moon*' is other than that of the words 'Deimos and Phobos'; and the sentence 'the number of Deimos and Phobos is two,' if it expresses any thought at all, at least expresses a different one from the sentence 'the number of Martian moons is two.' Since sentences of the first form are never used to make a numerical statement, the author misses the sense of such statements.

IV. *On 'General' or 'Common' Names*

p. 326] Later on, Husserl (p. 156) quotes my words: 'If we use 1 to symbolize each of the objects to be numbered, that is a mistake, for different things get the same symbol. If we supply the 1 with diacritical marks, it becomes useless for arithmetic.' His comment (p. 165) is: 'We commit this mistake every time we apply general names. If we call Hans, Kunz, etc., each one "a man," we have the same case as the "erroneous notation" in which when counting we write 1 for each of the objects to be counted.' If we did designate Hans by 'man,' and Kunz likewise, we should indeed be committing this mistake. Fortunately this is not what we do. If we call Hans a man, what we are saying is that Hans falls under the concept *man*; we are not writing or saying 'man' instead of 'Hans.' What would correspond to the sentence 'Hans is a man' is 'Hans is a 1.' If we call A, B, in the sense of giving A

the proper name '*B*,' then naturally we can always say '*B*' instead of '*A*'; but then we may not give the same proper name '*B*' to another object. The unfortunate expression 'common name' has assuredly been responsible for this confusion. The so-called common name—which would be better called 'concept word'—has nothing to do with objects directly, but stands for a concept. Under this concept objects may fall; but it may also be empty, and this does not stop the concept word from standing for p. 327] something. I have already given an adequate exposition of this point in § 47 of my *Foundations of Arithmetic*. It is surely clear that when anyone uses the sentence 'all men are mortal' he does not want to assert something about some Chief Akpanya, of whom perhaps he has never heard.

V. On 1 and 0; are they Numbers?

p. 327] We now pass on to the second difficulty, over the numbers 1 and 0. It is easy to find the first way out of it: you say they are not numbers at all. But now the question arises: In that case what are they? The author says (p. 144) : negative answers to the question 'how many?'; answers like 'never' to the question 'when?' 'Not-many or "no plurality "is not a particular case of many' (p. 144). Somebody may go on to think that two is still not many but only two (duality as opposed to plurality), so that *none*, *one*, and *two* are the three negative answers to the question 'How many?'; he might cite in confirmation of this the fact that two is the only even prime number. It is really too much to want us to regard as negative the answer 'one' to the question 'How many moons has the Earth?' As regards nought, the thing is more specious. What is the right view of answers like the answers 'never,' 'nowhere,' 'nothing' to the questions 'when?' 'where?' 'what?' Clearly, they are not proper answers but refusals to answer, which have the form of an answer. We say : 'I cannot tell you a time, a place, an object, of the desired sort, for there is none.' What would correspond to this is the following sort of reply to the question 'how many?': 'I cannot tell you any such number, for there is none.' On account of my view as to the sense of numerical statements, that would be my reply, e.g., to the question 'How many is Great Britain and Ireland?' I cannot regard either the answer 'nought' or the answer 'one' to the question 'How many?' as equivalent to 'There is no such number.' How is it that we have here two negative replies? When we give the reply 'nobody' to the question 'who was Romulus's predecessor on the throne of Rome?' we are denying that anybody did precede Romulus. The negation thus goes along with the predicate, and is fused with the grammatical subject in a logically incorrect fashion, so that it looks as though 'nobody,' like 'Romulus,' designated a man. This notoriously makes certain fallacies possible. One might think that such dangers threatened us also in the case of nought and one; but we use them just like other numbers, without special precautions. Why the difference? The answer 'nought' is no more a negative answer to the question 'What is the number of Romulus's predecessors on the throne of Rome?' than the answer 'two' would be. We are not denying that there is such a number, but naming the number.

VI. *On Abstraction*

p. 323] The author himself finds a difficulty about the abstraction that provides the general concept of the collective. He says (p. 84): 'The peculiarities of the individual contents that are collected . . . must be completely abstracted from, but at the same time their connexion must be maintained. This seems to involve a difficulty, if not a psychological impossibility. If we take the abstraction seriously, then the individual contents vanish, and so, naturally, does their collective unity, instead of remaining behind p. 324] as a conceptual extract. The solution is obvious. To abstract from something simply means: not to attend to it specially.'

The kernel of this explanation is obviously to be found in the word 'specially'. Inattention is a very strong lye; it must be applied at not too great a concentration, so that everything does not dissolve, and likewise not too dilute, so that it effects a sufficient change in the things. Thus it is a question of getting the right degree of dilution; this is difficult to manage, and I at any rate have never succeeded.

. . . .

p. 316] [Detaching our attention] is particularly effective. We attend less to a property, and it disappears. By making one characteristic after another disappear, we get more and more abstract concepts. . . . Inattention is a most efficacious logical faculty; presumably this accounts for the absentmindedness of professors. Suppose there are a black and a white cat sitting side by side before us. We stop attending to their colour, and they become colourless, but are still sitting side by side. We stop attending to their posture, and they are no longer sitting (though they have not assumed another posture), but each one is still in p. 317] its place. We stop attending to position; they cease to have place, but still remain different. In this way, perhaps, we obtain from each one of them a general concept of Cat. By continued application of this procedure, we obtain from each object a more and more bloodless phantom. Finally we thus obtain from each object a *something* wholly deprived of content; but the *something* obtained from one object is different from the *something* obtained from another object—though it is not easy to say how. . . . On my view, bringing an object under a concept is just recognition of a relation that was there already; here, objects are essentially altered by abstraction, so that objects brought under one concept become more alike.

A CRITICAL ELUCIDATION OF SOME POINTS IN E. SCHROEDER'S *VORLESUNGEN UEBER DIE ALGEBRA DER LOGIK**

First published in *Archiv für systematische Philosophie*, vol. 1 (1895), pp. 433-456

HERR SCHRÖDER rejects Boole's *universe of discourse* in virtue of a peculiar consideration, which I should like to subject here to a more exact inquiry; for in this way there is made apparent the necessity of a distinction that seems to be unknown to many logicians.

For the sake of intelligibility, it will be desirable to begin by presenting the main lines of Schroder's domain-calculus. As the author expounds it, the calculus is always intertwined with logic proper; and this makes it difficult to see into the heart of the matter. So, to begin with, I here leave logic quite out of consideration, in order that the peculiarity of this calculus may be better brought out.

Following Herr Schröder, we imagine given to us a manifold of elements. The nature of this manifold and its elements is not in question, and so any manifold can represent any other. To p. 434] make the matter intuitively clear it is best to consider the manifold of points on a plane surface, or the manifold of areas into which such a surface is divided by two sets of parallel straight lines, so that no two areas have a point in common. 'Any aggregation of elements of the manifold we call a *domain* of the latter,' (p. 157). The most important relation that can hold between domains is represented to be inclusion; this is taken to mean that the first domain is contained in the second, and to cover the case where the two domains coincide. About this relation of inclusion we now get two axioms laid down:

1. Every domain is included in itself.
2. If one domain is included in a second, and this in a third, then the first is likewise included in the third.

* Teubner, Leipzig. In what follows page-references are to the first volume.

Instead of 'domains' we may here always also say 'classes,' if we take classes to be collective wholes, such as a wood, for example, and do not bring them into connexion with concepts. Of course usage is always likely to mislead us here, since it suggests expressions like 'classes of men, of trees,' etc., in which a concept is mentioned every time. What Herr Schröder calls 'inclusion' or 'subsumption' is here, properly speaking, nothing but the part-whole relation, extended in such a way that every whole is to be treated as a part of itself. From the point of view we are now adopting, we do not need the words 'individual' and 'single thing.' Divisibility can be imagined as going on *ad infinitum*. Thus, moreover, the expression 'element' has as yet no importance here, properly speaking; for it is all one whether in the example mentioned above we choose to regard as elements the square areas of which the surface consists or (say) the triangles into which these are divided by their diagonals. If we take the German Army as our manifold and an infantry regiment as a domain within it, it is all one whether we choose to regard as elements the battalions, the companies, or the single soldiers. Thus it is all one so far which parts of the whole shall be called elements, p. 435] so long as any domain we consider can be compounded out of them; and we have no need at all to assume that there are parts insusceptible of further division; so perhaps it is better at this stage not to talk about elements at all. Like the word 'class,' the word 'manifold' also may produce obscurity; for it is often used in conjunction with a concept-word, e.g. 'manifold of points,' 'manifold of trees,' etc.; and in this way something logical gets mixed up with our discussion, whereas for the time being we still have to keep that out. So in order to develop the domain-calculus in its full purity we do best to avoid the words 'manifold,' 'class,' 'element,' 'subsumption,' and use instead of 'manifold' something like 'super-domain.'

I give some passages from Schröder's book that support this view of the domain-calculus. 'And *one* individual may likewise be termed a class—one that contains only this individual itself. . . . But also any class that itself contains many individuals can again be represented as an object of thought and accordingly as an individual (in a broader sense, e.g. as a 'relative' individual in regard to higher classes)' (p. 148). Here there is indeed talk of individuals; but we also see straightaway that the distinction between individual and class is treated as a fluctuating one. It is apparent from several passages that a class is to be viewed as a totality of objects, a collective unity. Thus, on p. 67 there is talk about individual things making up a class. The class is called a collection (p. 83). 'We are able to take any objects of thought whatsoever as "individuals" and unite, "combine" them into a "class" ' (p. 148). We saw above that a class may coincide with a single individual, and so, in that case, consists of it. So also we read on p. 150 'If we say "some men are shrewd," the subject is a class consisting of an indefinite number of men, "some" men.' Let us observe that on this showing a class consists of objects. Admittedly we have here already an admixture of logic. On p. 161 we have: 'We are led on to this field of application (β), to which we now go on from (α), through noticing, having it pointed out, that the "elements" of our manifold can also p. 436] be so-called "*individuals*," and then the "domains" of this manifold will have to be termed "systems," "*classes*" if you like, of such individuals.' Here it is to be observed that in Schröder's use of language 'system' stands for a collective unity (pp. 71-2).

Up to this point everything is consistent; and moreover the definition of the 'identical' sum (p. 196) may be admitted, in spite of its not being logically unexceptionable, if we throw in the interpretation on p. 217; according to this, 'identical' addition results in an aggregation or collection of the two classes; the individuals of the two classes are thereby collected or 'gathered together' into a single class. Here too the so-called individuals may be themselves assumed to be further divisible *ad libitum* without our meeting with any difficulties. This 'identical' addition, like everything that has gone before, admits of an excellent intuitive representation in Euler's diagrams.

But now we are approaching the point where the pure domain-calculus is no longer adequate and the analogy of the Euler diagrams becomes a lame one. In fact, the pure domain-calculus is quite unfruitful; and its apparent fruitfulness in this book arises just because it is not pure; something logical is always intruding, a thing that happens almost imperceptibly by way of the words 'manifold,' 'individual,' 'class,' 'subsumption.'

We pass on to 'identical' multiplication; by the interpretation on p. 217, this results from isolation or selection; we 'gather out' from one class those individuals that belong to another. Even here, the basis of the way of thinking we have adopted so far need not always be abandoned; and Euler's diagrams can still be used, so long as the areas of the plane answering to the two classes have a part in common. In that case, this part is precisely a representation of the 'identical' product. But what if the areas have no part in common? For classes too there arises the case where two of them have no part in common. A class, in the sense in which we have so far used the word, consists of objects; it is an aggregate, a collective unity, of them; if so, it must vanish when p. 437] these objects vanish. If we burn down all the trees of a wood, we thereby burn down the wood. Thus there can be no empty class. Now if we said that there is not always an 'identical' product, and inquired each time whether there were one before we made use of it, all would be in order, but the calculus would be grievously crippled. Herr Schröder pays no heed to this; he speaks of an empty class (p. 147) and uses the 'identical' product in his calculations without more ado; he thus departs from the basis of the pure domain-calculus. He relies here on the *'identical'* zero, of which he says (p. 197) that its mission is to earn us the right of always being able to speak of the 'identical' product. One may ask: What then earns us the right to speak of the 'identical' zero? But let us leave this question on one side for the moment.

We must next bring into our discussion the logical aspect that has so far been kept out. According to the author, the transition would be made somewhat as follows. The 'identical' calculus, which is originally a pure domain-calculus, nevertheless admits of various sorts of application (p. 160). We obtain logic in this way: the letters that we have so far interpreted as domains we now interpret as classes—as concepts taken in extension. Of course if we kept to the use of the word 'class' that we have adopted so far, then we should not have anything new. Classes in this sense are not to be distinguished from domains. But if we take classes to be extensions of concepts; and if the relation of inclusion, also called subsumption, which was nothing over and above the relation of part to whole, is now replaced by the relation that holds between the extensions when one concept is subordinate to the other; we are then entering on quite a new field. Herr Schröder admittedly does not seem to take proper notice of this. He does indeed count this way of applying the calculus under the heading (β) (p. 160), and so places it side by side with the 'domain' interpretation mentioned under (α), as something different; but when he says (p. 161) that the elements of our manifold may also be '*individuals*' and that in this case the 'domains' of the manifold are to be termed 'systems,' or, if you p. 438] like, '*classes*' of such individuals, then he is thinking of this as just a particular case. On this showing classes are also domains, and it needs no proof that the laws of domain-calculus are still valid here. But because of the connexion established between classes and concepts, viz. that classes are to be the extensions of concepts, the matter nevertheless assumes a new aspect; this is shown externally, in the first instance, in the new translations given for the formulae. What has so far been properly translatable as '*A* is a part of *B*' is now to be rendered as 'all *A*s are *B*s.' I should first like to point out a small inaccuracy. If we take *A* and *B* to be classes or extensions of concepts, then we cannot say 'all *A*s are *B*s,' for here *A* and *B* are used in a different sense. If, e.g., *A* is the extension of the concept *square*, and *B* the extension of the concept *rectangle*, we cannot say 'all extension of the concept *square* is extension of the concept *rectangle*,' or 'all extensions of the concept *square* are extensions of the concept *rectangle*,' or 'the extension of the concept *square* is the extension of the concept *rectangle*.' Herr Schröder, who elsewhere laudably practices accuracy of language, has unfortunately here been untrue to his habit, and has thus obscured the matter. We now also have *A* called the subject and *B* the predicate (pp. 132-3), or again they are called the subject-concept and the predicate-concept. This too is inexact, unless the expressions 'concept' and 'extension of a concept' are being used as equivalents. Again, the sign of inclusion, which previously expressed *A*'s being a part of *B*, now has to correspond to the copula '*is*' or '*are*' (pp. 132-3). But if instead of 'all mammals are vertebrates' we say 'the class of mammals is included in the class of vertebrates,' the predicate is not *the class of vertebrates* but *included in the class of vertebrates*;

and *is included* is not the copula alone but the copula *plus* a bit of the predicate.

All sorts of things have got out of order here; and the bad consequences of this will be immediately apparent now that we are proceeding to Schröder's rejection of Boole's *universe of* p. 439] *discourse.* The author has always spoken of a manifold, containing the classes or domains within which the movement of thought occurs in a given case. This manifold is named 1; and Herr Schröder now tries to show that it is not all-embracing like Boole's *universe of discourse.* On p. 245 we have:

'As we have laid down, 0 would have to be contained in *every* class that can be got out of the manifold 1; . . . 0 would have to be a subject to *every* predicate.'

'Now suppose we took *a* to be *the class of those classes of the manifold that are equal to* 1 (which would certainly be permissible if we could bring everything thinkable into the manifold 1), then this class of its very nature contains just one class, viz. the symbol 1 itself, or alternatively the whole of the manifold, which constitutes the reference of the symbol; *but therefore besides this it would contain* "*nothing,*" i.e. 0. Hence 1 and 0 would make up the class of the objects that are to be equal to 1; and so we should have to admit not only: 1 = 1 but *also*: 0 = 1. For a predicate that applies to a class—in our case, the predicate: to be identically equal to 1—must also apply to every individual in the class, by Principle II.'

On p. 246 the author shows that we can apply these considerations to any class *b* of the manifold, instead of 1, and thus reaches the conclusion 0 = *b*. This contradiction comes like a thunderbolt from a clear sky. How could we be prepared for anything like this in exact logic! Who can go surety for it that we shall not again suddenly encounter a contradiction as we go on? The possibility of such a thing points to a mistake in the original design. Herr Schröder derives from this the conclusion that the original manifold 1 must be so made up that, among the elements given as individuals within it, there are found no classes that, for their part, contain within themselves as individuals any elements of the same manifold. This expedient, as it were, belatedly gets the ship off the sandbank; but if she had been properly steered, she could have kept off it altogether. It now

becomes clear why at the very outset, in shrewd prevision of the
p. 440] imminent danger, a certain manifold was introduced as
the theatre of operation, although there was no reason for this
in the pure domain-calculus. The subsequent restriction of this
field for our logical activities is by no means elegant. Whereas
elsewhere logic may claim to have laws of unrestricted validity,
we are here required to begin by delimiting a manifold with care-
ful tests, and it is only then that we can move around inside it.
A consequence of this is that the 'identical' zero likewise depends
on the delimitation of the manifold. Thus it may come about
that what is something in one manifold is zero or nothing in the
other. Now negation is defined in terms of o and 1 (p. 302),
and therefore this also depends on the manifold chosen, so that a
class *a* may perhaps be the negation of *b* in one manifold, but not
in another. Hence in a rigorously scientific statement one would
always have to give an exact specification of the manifold
within which the inquiry is being carried out. Now this suggests
the question whether these inconveniences cannot be avoided,
and what is the advantage anyhow in this restriction of the theatre
of operations.

When Herr Schröder stipulates (p. 248), as regards the original
manifold, that among the elements given as 'individuals' there
shall be found no classes that, for their part, comprise within them
as individuals any elements of the same manifold, he is obviously
distinguishing the case where something is given as an individual
belonging to a manifold or class, where something is comprised
within a class as an individual, from the case where something is
contained as a class within a manifold or class. Herr Husserl makes
a similar distinction, in his review* of Schröder's work, between
the expressions 'a class contains something as an element' and 'a
class contains something as a sub-class,' and by this he tries to remove the difficulty. The important thing here is that our attention is drawn to the essential difference between two relations, for
p. 441] which the author uses the same sign (the sign of '*eventuelle*
Subordination' or inclusion). We see again from this that we are
not no longer standing on the basis of the domain-calculus; for
there we had only the part-whole relation, and there was no

* *Göttingische gelehrte Anzeigen*, 1891, p. 272.

grourd for this distinction between the cases where a class contains something as an individual and where it contains it as a class. The Euler diagrams are a lame analogy for logical relations, since they do not bring out this important distinction.*

In order to bring clarity into the matter, it will be necessary to correct Schröder's mistake, and, when things are different, to use different signs for them. So we lay it down that

$$\text{`} A \; sub \; B \text{'}$$

is to assert that A is a class subordinate to the class B. On the other hand

$$\text{`} A \; subter \; B \text{'}$$

is to express A's being comprised as an individual under the class B. In doing this we have of course done no more than just to recognize that there is a difference; we still do not know exactly what it consists in. Anyhow, we can now express Schröder's stipulation as follows: The manifold A must be so made up that p. 442] for no A and B are the propositions:

$$B \; subter \; M$$
$$A \; subter \; B$$
$$A \; subter \; M$$

true simultaneously. Now how does this avoid the absurdity that apparently we can prove $o = b$? That conclusion was possible only because of the interpretation that Herr Schröder gives to his formulae by bringing classes into connexion with

---

* To be sure, not all of those who inveigh against Euler's diagrams show any better understanding of the matter. When, in the judgment 'some numbers are primes,' they regard 'some numbers' as the subject; or when, in the judgment 'all bodies are heavy,' they represent 'all bodies,' or the concept *bodies* in its full extension, as the subject; what lies at the bottom of this is just the superficial view as to the concept (one might call it a mechanical or quantitative view) that comes out also in Euler's diagrams. If we negate such sentences, the sign of negation must come before 'some' or 'all,' and this makes it clear that so far as their sense goes these words must be counted in with the predicative part of the sentence. The word 'some' states a relation that holds (in our example) between the concepts 'number' and 'prime.' Similarly 'all' in the second example states a relation between the concepts *bodies* and *heavy*. An expression answering better to the logical structure is: 'bodies are universally heavy.' Herr Schröder gives an example (p. 180) of *quaternio terminorum* that arises because the expression 'some gentlemen' does not always designate the same part of the class of gentlemen. Accordingly such an expression would have to be rejected as ambiguous; and it must, in fact, be rejected if one regards it (like our author, p. 150) as designating a class that consists of 'some' gentlemen. Of course what I am here rejecting is not the particular judgment, but only a wrong conception of it.

concepts; in the pure domain-calculus there is no occasion for the absurdity to arise. It becomes necessary, and possible, to distinguish between the *sub*-relation and the *subter*-relation only when we leave the pure domain-calculus—as soon as we adopt the mode of interpretation mentioned above, and thus bring concepts into the discussion, and pass over into the domain of logic. So if we want to make clear to ourselves the distinction between the two relations, we must regard classes as extensions of concepts and make this the basis of our interpretation.

Accordingly, let us make trial of the following rules:

If v is a single thing and A is the class of things that *are* a, then we interpret

$$\text{`}v \; subter \; A\text{'}$$

to mean 'v is an a'; and if B is the class of objects that *are* b, we translate

$$\text{`}B \; sub \; A\text{'}$$

by 'all b's are a's.'*

It must here be further noticed that *is* or *are* in italics is to be regarded as the mere copula, with no particular content at all, and that thus no identity is meant.

Let us now discuss more precisely the possibility of our sophism. To this end, we need to decide whether in Schröder's definition of the 'identical' zero the relation of being included is to be taken as the *sub* or the *subter* relation. It runs, in fact, as follows: 'o is our name for a domain that stands to every domain a in the relation of being included' (p. 188). Thus the question is whether zero is subordinate, as a class, to every class of the p. 443] manifold, or whether zero is comprised as an individual within every class of the manifold. Let us first try the latter assumption. In that case

$$\text{o} \; subter \; a$$

will hold when

$$a \; sub \; M$$

does, where M is to be our manifold. Now let Q be the class of

---

* Signor G. Peano uses instead of '*sub*' and '*subter*' the signs '⊃' and 'ϵ.' See *Notations de logique mathématique*, par G. Peano; Turin 1894; §6.

objects that coincide with P. Then P is the only individual comprised within Q, and we have

$$P \; subter \; Q.$$

Now if Q *sub* M holds, then we have also, in accordance with our supposition about zero,

$$o \; subter \; Q$$

i.e. o coincides with P. This possibility is of course removed by the author's stipulation. For from

$$P \; subter \; Q$$
$$\text{and } Q \; sub \; M$$
there follows P *subter* M.

Now, on the other hand, P is the same as Q; the class Q, in fact, contracts into P. Thus Q *subter* M also holds, and we have:

$$Q \; subter \; M,$$
$$P \; subter \; Q,$$
$$P \; subter \; M,$$

contrary to Schröder's stipulation. A doubt might arise over the question whether Q coincides with P. At any rate this answers perfectly to the view of the class as consisting of single things. In line with this we read on p. 247: 'And in particular the individuals (of the manifold) themselves belong among the classes; in this case, since they contract to just one individual, we may use the term "monadic" or "*singular*" classes.' And we thus get on p. 148: 'And *one* individual may likewise be termed a class—one that contains only this individual itself.' In the light of this it can scarcely be doubted that on Schröder's principles Q in our case coincides with P.

At this point, however, we encounter a peculiar difficulty. p. 444] If a class that consists of just one object coincides with this object, then Schröder's stipulation cannot be satisfied for any manifold that contains individuals at all. Let *a* be such an individual, so that we have:

$$a \; subter \; M.$$

Then *a* itself belongs among the classes, and is in fact a singular class, so that we have:

$$a \; subter \; a.$$

Thus the stipulation that for no A and B shall we have simultaneously

$$B \text{ subter } M,$$
$$A \text{ subter } B,$$
$$\text{and: } A \text{ subter } M,$$

cannot be satisfied; for if we take both A and B to be a, we get our present case. Now Herr Schröder writes: 'Even if we constructed only one singular (class) in this (manifold), and admitted it as a new individual, the identical zero would at once intrude into the class; would slip in, so to speak, through the door of Def. (2x)' (p. 248). This is not in accord with the principles elsewhere expressed by the author. For, by these, there is no need at all for a singular class to be constructed first; if a is an individual in the manifold, then a already is also a class; and it is unnecessary to go on and admit a into the manifold as a new individual, for a is there already. Moreover, what is required in order that the 'identical' zero should slip into a class is *not* that the class should be given as an individual in a manifold, but that it should be included in the manifold as a (sub-)class. It is not the *subter* but the *sub* relation that is in question.

The doubt whether each individual may be regarded as the class that consists of it alone is made stronger by the following consideration. In the discussion set forth above we may take P to be itself likewise a class comprising a number of individuals; for, as the author says (p. 148), such a class can be presented as an object of thought and consequently as an individual. Now if Q, as before, is the class of objects that coincide with P, then Q is a p. 445] singular class containing only P as an individual. Now if it were right to hold that a singular class coincides with the only individual it contains, then Q would coincide with P. Let us now suppose that a and b are different objects, contained within P as individuals; then they would also be contained within Q; i.e. both a and b would coincide with P. Consequently a would also coincide with b, contrary to our permissible supposition that they are different. The author would perhaps object to our bringing a and b into the matter at all, because by his stipulation they could not be counted among the elements of the manifold. But as we have seen already, this stipulation cannot be satisfied anyhow, on our present supposition; so it must be abandoned.

Now our supposition that singular classes coincide with individuals is a necessary inference from the conception that classes consist of individuals—a view that accords with, and arises out of, the domain-calculus. As we see here, this conception is not suitable for logical use; and the domain-calculus, far from being profitable for logic, here shows itself merely misleading. It is worth our notice that this last discussion need make no reference at all to the 'identical' zero; and thus the force of the proof does not depend in any way on whether the definition of this zero can be upheld.

We have seen that the conception of the class as consisting of individuals, so that the single thing coincides with the singular class, cannot be upheld in any case—whether we retain or abandon Schröder's stipulation. In the latter case, the conception leads to contradictions; in the former, we must abandon it if we are to make Schröder's stipulation at all realizable. Moreover, it follows that our sophism cannot be avoided by the stipulation.

Let us, for example, take as our manifold the manifold of integers. The class of numbers coincident with 3 contains no individual but the number 3 itself. Let us first suppose that the p. 446] number 3 is this singular class; then this class is given as an individual in the manifold, and contains the number 3 as an individual within itself—which is in its turn an element in the manifold, contrary to Schröder's stipulation. Let us secondly suppose that the singular class just mentioned does not coincide with 3 or with any other integer. In that case the class would not be given as an individual in our manifold, and Schröder's stipulation would be fulfilled; but on the other hand our sophism would be possible. For this singular class would comprise 3 as an individual within it; but it would likewise contain the 'identical' zero; i.e. the 'identical' zero would coincide with the number 3, and likewise with every integer; so all integers would coincide.

At this point, however, there arises the doubt whether on the author's view there can be singular classes at all containing any individual other than o. For if a class contracts to an individual *a*, then we have:

a subter a
and also: o *subter a*.

So if *a* is different from o, the class *a* contains within it the individuals a and o, and is thus *not* a singular class. The 'identical' zero always slips in as well. Cf., however, the following passage (p. 241): 'We have seen that o means "nothing"; the sign "*subter*"* answers to the copula and must be translated "is" in ordinary language; finally, *a* may be any arbitrary predicate†— let us say for instance "black." The subsumption o *subter a* is undoubtedly correct, since the class of all the things we should call black contains nothing besides these, and so, as I may put it, over and above these it contains "nothing." '

Let us now take *a* to be the class consisting of the Moon and the 'identical' zero: then 'o *subter a*' would have to be understood, according to Herr Schröder, as: the class *a* contains nothing besides the Moon; or as: the class a contains the Moon and over and above that it also contains 'nothing.' The first expression p. 447] would lead one to think that this class was a singular one and contained only the Moon; but by the second expression it looks as though it contained the identical zero as well as the Moon, and were thus not a singular class. Cf. what the author says on p. 197: 'There is at least one domain *c* that satisfies the hypotheses of Def. (3), for by Def. (2x) . . . at any rate o is such a *c*.' The visual field of our mind's eye is now in the same state as that of our bodily eyes when one of them is looking through a blue, and the other through a yellow, glass; one moment there is nothing, next moment there is something. Are we not here befooled by language, because negation, which really belongs with the predicate, is amalgamated with another constituent of the sentence to form a spurious proper name? If we say that the class *a* contains nothing besides the Moon, then we are denying the proposition that the class contains something besides the Moon; but we are not thereby asserting that the class contains, besides the Moon, an object with the name 'nothing.'

---

* Here I replace Schröder's sign by *subter*, in accordance with what we are assuming to be the sense of the definition of the identical zero.

† The author is here referring to the requirement he imposes on the manifold.

Thus language produces for us a mirage of an object; and Herr Schröder seems to be doing the same, when he speaks of his 'identical' zero. And yet he himself surely recognizes that a name must be a name for something. For after calling a name many-sensed when it does not satisfy the requirement of univocality, he goes on (p. 50): 'so long, that is, as it . . . has a sense at all, really is a name *for something*, i.e. so long as we are leaving out of account . . . only senseless or "*nonsense*" names, like "round square" . . .' Isn't 'the identical zero' such a senseless or nonsense name? The affirmative answer is implied by the author's calling the name 'nothing' senseless and meaningless (p. 69); for 'nothing,' as we have seen, is his rendering for his zero (p. 189).

This is the place for discussing more precisely the definition of the 'identical' zero. It runs thus (p. 188):

'We must now go on to introduce two special domains into the algebra of logic; the numerals 0 and 1 recommend themselves . . . as names for these. We want to define these also by means of the relational sign for inclusion; and in fact the definition (2x) of the "*identical zero*" is to follow from our presenting the subsumption

p. 448]   0 *subter a**

as a *generally valid* one, i.e. one that must be recognized as holding for *every* domain of our manifold. This means to say: 0 *is our name for a domain that* stands to every domain *a* in the relation of being included—*is contained in every domain of the manifold.*'

By its phraseology this definition belongs entirely to the domain-calculus, but it is irreconcilable with it as regards its sense. An objection that we previously postponed must now be more precisely examined. After the definitions of his 0 and 1 Herr Schröder goes on as follows:

'The symbols 0 and 1 to which we ascribe these properties are in any case henceforth counted among the "domains" of our manifold. Eventually they will perhaps turn out to be "improper" domains; i.e. they are still empty names, if it should prove impossible to point them out among the actual or proper domains that have been regarded as such so far, that appear to be virtually or potentially given to us at the same time as the manifold.'

---

* Here I write '*subter*' in place of Schröder's inclusion-sign.

Here we are first struck by the confusion between sign and thing signified. In the definition itself the author says: 'o is our name for a domain . . .' and from this it clearly follows that the zero-sign is to be a name for something that is a domain. In the explanation just quoted, the signs themselves suddenly appear as domains. This confusion is so dear to the author that he cannot abandon it, in spite of my admonitions.*

Now for zero the circumstance foreseen in this explanation does actually arise. There is in fact, e.g., no domain contained in all the domains of the States of the German Empire. Herr Schröder does not let this worry him. For him, definition guarantees the existence of the thing defined, inasmuch as it itself, after a fashion, generates or creatively introduces it (p. 212); p. 449] very much after a fashion, of course! By definition, the symbol o has had assigned to it the property of being included in every domain of the manifold; and thus, by means of this creative definition, we have now got a domain that is contained in every domain of our manifold. Of course this is only an empty sign; but since it has the desired property, we have all that we need. At least, so Herr Schröder thinks. The mistake he commits here is a favourite one with mathematicians, and I have repeatedly called attention to it without making any impression; I suppose one must infer from this that mathematicians have a well-established prescriptive right to their procedure. For logicians it is otherwise. On the other hand, it is to be desired that no such right should come into being in their case; as a bar to this, I hope the present statement still does not come too late. If the zero-sign is an empty sign, then it designates nothing; and thus as a sign it misses its end, at least so far as science is concerned (and in fiction, for that matter, there will hardly be any use for it). The author himself says (p. 128) that when we put one thing equal to another, or express or assert identity, the question is not about the sound of names, or about how expressions may look, but entirely and solely about what these *stand for*.† But what if there is nothing they do stand for? The zero-sign is an oval figure

* Cf. my *Grundlagen der Arithmetik* (Koebner, Breslau, 1884), p. 54 and p. 95 footnote. On p. 200 the author uses the phrase 'an *a* that means zero'; does *a* here 'mean' the zero-sign, or the meaning that this hasn't got?

† On p. 199, to be sure, he requires that Principle I (the principle of Identity) shall be admitted also for names—regardless of whether they have a sense or not.

made, e.g., on paper with printer's ink. Now what more does the definition do? Can it endow this figure with any new property whatsoever? On the contrary, the very most that the figure can get is the property of serving as a sign for the thing that we fix upon as its reference. Or does this figure become a domain contained in every domain of some manifold or other, simply in virtue of my saying it is such a domain? If that were possible, it might also not be hard to make diamonds. Now Herr Schröder himself in the definition does not in fact say that this figure is such a domain, but only that it is to be a sign or name for such a domain. He thus attempts an act of naming, and it could be foreseen that the attempt must fail; for an act of naming involves p. 450] above all something that is named, and here this is lacking. Now how can such an abortive attempt make any difference at all to that which was chosen to be a name or sign? Thus in the domain-calculus the definition must be rejected. But just the same holds true of the logical calculus; for there is not a thing that is contained as an individual within every class of a manifold, at any rate not if more than one class is contained in the manifold; and this is always the case if empty classes are admitted and the manifold is not empty. If, however, it is empty, there is nothing at all to be contained in a class of the manifold.

No wonder that such a faulty definition leads to contradictions! We can certainly count as another of these what the author says on p. 238: ' "*Nothing*" *is thus a subject to every predicate*: Nothing is black, at the same time Nothing is also not black.' Assertions of the form '*a* is *b*' and '*a* is not *b*' assuredly constitute a contradiction. Herr Schröder would perhaps add: if they are not devoid of content; but if they are, they are properly speaking not assertions at all, but nonsense; and all that logic can do with nonsense is to recognize it as such—it cannot make use of it.

Let us now consider the other way of taking our definition. We may replace Schröder's sign of inclusion by '*sub*.' In that case, therefore,

$$0 \; sub \; a$$

is to hold good generally, for any class* *a* within the manifold.

* I here write 'class' instead of 'domain,' because in the domain-calculus neither the *sub* nor the *subter* relation occurs, but only the part-whole relation.

Here, too, we must regard o and *a* as extensions of concepts in order to get a sense for 'o *sub a.*' Accordingly o will have to be regarded as a class of objects that have a certain property. Let us say for short that o is the class of objects that are *b*,* postponing the decision what '*b*' must be taken to mean. Further, let *a* be the class of objects that are *c*.* Then

$$o \; sub \; a$$

p. 451] must be taken to mean: 'all *bs* are *c*'; and this is to hold for any arbitrary class *a*, so long as it is contained in our manifold. Now if there were a single thing *v* that was a *b*,

$$v \; subter \; o,^{A}$$

then we should also have

$$v \; subter \; a;$$

and this would have to hold good for any class *a* in our manifold, which, as I have said, is impossible. The only possibility remaining is that there is no single object that is a *b*—in short, that there is no *b*. In that case o is an empty class. But there cannot be an empty class if we take a class to be a collection or totality of individuals, so that, as the author says (p. 67),† the class consists of individuals or individuals make up the class. In the course of this discussion we have once more had it shown to us that this way of talking is logically useless; that the extension of a concept is constituted in being, not by the individuals, but by the concept itself; i.e. by what is asserted of an object when it is brought under a concept. There is then no objection to our talking about the class of objects that are *bs* even when there are no *bs*. Moreover, all empty concepts now have the same extension.‡ We can, e.g., take *b* to be *object that is not the same as itself.* If we now call the extension of this concept o, then the question is how in that case we are to take the proposition 'o *sub a*' or 'all *bs* are *c*.' Herr Schröder (p. 239) reads it in this case as meaning 'all *bs*, in so far as there are any, are *c*,' or: '*either* there are no *bs*;^{B} *or*, if

* This 'are' must be regarded as a mere copula. Cf. p. 442 *supra.*
† We can, however, also find assertions opposed to this. On p. 147 he says that the concept of class must not be taken too narrowly, and thus empty classes also are admitted. To be sure, the way this is to be reconciled with the other assertions remains obscure.
‡ Cf. also my *Grundgesetze der Arithmetik*, Hermann Pohle, Jena, 1893; §§ 3 and 10.

A In the original text, *v subter b*; '*b*' is certainly a misprint for 'o'.
B '*a*' misprinted for '*b*' in the original.

there are any, then all of them are *c*.' I can agree to this way of taking it, for it is a suitable way and the only way that is of any use in logic, even though it does some violence to usage. Accordingly

0 *sub a*

p. 452] must be rendered: 'either there are no objects that are not the same as themselves; or, if there are any, then all of them are *c*.' There is nothing to be said against this; and so we have a class such that it is *sub a* whatever class *a* may be. And the zero-sign now really does stand for something with the property required by our definition.

Let us now inquire whether the sophism that provoked this whole discussion is possible. Let Q be once more the class of objects that coincide with P. We have now

0 *sub* Q;

i.e. 'either there are no objects that are not the same as themselves; or, if there are any, they all coincide with P.' This proposition is unexceptionable, and there can be no question of a sophism. So in this case we simply do not need to confine our thought to a manifold that satisfies certain requirements; when once we avoid a mistake in definition, everything falls into proper order.

In support of many of the assertions that I have here been expounding, passages could be quoted from Schröder also; but so could passages contradicting them. What can be the source of this inconsistency? Herr Schröder, as he says in his Introduction, found great difficulties in the theory of the construction of concepts, and in explaining their nature. He observed the battle over these questions wavering endlessly this way and that without being decided. He wanted to escape this uncertainty by founding logic not on the content of concepts but on the extension, and he thought he could here leave it undecided how the delimitation of classes comes about. This led him to the domain-calculus, to the view that classes consist of single things, are collections of individuals; for in fact what else is there to constitute a class, if we ignore the concepts, the common properties! The single thing is then likewise a class. The natural result is that the fundamental relation is that of part to whole. All this is intuitively very clear, and indubitable; only unfortunately it is barren, and it is not logic. Only because classes are determined p. 453] by the properties that individuals in them are to have, and because we use phrases like this: 'the class of objects that are *b*'; only so does it become possible to express thoughts in general by stating relations between classes; only so do we get a logic. The complete difference, and indeed incompatibility, between this conception of classes and the one first mentioned is, of course, concealed at first. Thus there arises a cruder conception of classes and extensions, side by side with a subtler one, the only one that can be used in logic; and the incompatibility of the two becomes noticeable only incidentally, by means of contradictions. It is understandable that this happens most obviously where there is no class in the 'domain-calculus' sense—when we have empty concepts. Somebody might have the idea of rejecting such concepts as illegitimate; but this would involve excluding from logic wide and particularly fruitful domains. Herr Schröder is quite right in not wanting to do this and in stressing the importance of introducing the 'identical' zero (p. 189)—though the recognition of empty concepts need not be made exactly in this form. If we admit a sentence 'there is a ——,' we may not exclude a sentence 'there is no ——'; for unless the negation of a sentence has a sense, the sentence itself is without sense.

We must here keep well apart two wholly different cases that are easily confused, because we speak of existence in both cases. In one case the question is whether a proper name designates, names, something; in the other, whether a concept takes objects under itself. If we use the words 'there is a ——' we have the latter case. Now a proper name that designates nothing has no logical justification, since in logic we are concerned with truth in the strictest sense of the word; it may on the other hand still be used in fiction and fable.* For concepts that do not comprehend anything under them it is quite different; they are entirely legitimate. The author confuses these two cases when he calls 'Nothing' and 'round square' alike senseless, nonsensical, or p. 454] meaningless names (pp. 50, 69). His 'Nothing' is in many cases, e.g. in the sentences 'Nothing is black' and 'Nothing

---

* Cf. my paper *Ueber Sinn und Bedeutung, Zeitschrift für Phil. und phil. Kritik*, vol. 100.

is not black' (p. 238), a proper name without any reference, and hence logically illegitimate. 'Round square' on the other hand is not an empty name, but a name of an empty concept, and thus one not devoid of reference, in sentences like 'there is no round square' or 'the Moon is not a round square.' The word 'common name' is confusing here, for it makes it look as though the common name stood in the same, or much the same, relation to the objects that fall under the concept as the proper name does to a single object. Nothing could be more false! In this case it must, of course, appear as though a common name that belongs to an empty concept were as illegitimate as a proper name that designates nothing. The word 'planet' has no direct relation at all to the Earth, but only to a concept that the Earth, among other things, falls under; thus its relation to the Earth is only an indirect one, by way of the concept; and the recognition of this relation of *falling under* requires a judgment that is not in the least already given along with our knowledge of what the word 'planet' stands for. If I utter a sentence with the grammatical subject 'all men,' I do *not* wish to make an assertion about some Central African chief wholly unknown to me. It is thus utterly false that I am in any way designating this chief when I use the word 'man,' or that this chief belongs in any way whatsoever to the reference of the word 'man.' It is likewise equally false that in such a sentence many judgments are put together by means of the common name, as Herr Schröder thinks (p. 69). In order that a word like 'man' or 'planet' should have logical justification, it is necessary only that there should answer to it a sharply delimited concept; whether the concept comprehends something under itself is not here relevant.

It is easily seen how the use of the word 'common name' hangs together with the conception that the class or extension consists or is compounded of single things. In both cases the emphasis is laid on the things and the concept is overlooked. Now we do admittedly also get in Schröder's work passages like this: 'In this p. 455] way we show that for us what characterizes a concept . . . is just that a definite group of traits, distinguishable from all others . . . are associated and invariably correlated with its name' (pp. 89-90). But this is only another sign of the pervasive inconsistency that the author has not noticed and has thus not been able to escape.*

Someone may get the impression from my procedure that in the battle between extensionalist and intensionalist logicians I take ..e side of the latter. I do, in fact, maintain that the concept is logically prior to its extension; and I regard as futile the attempt to take the extension of a concept as a class, and make it rest, not on the concept, but on single things. That way we get a domain-calculus, not a logic. All the same, in many respects my position may be closer to the author than to those who could in contrast to him be termed intensionalist logicians.

In conclusion, we may sum up the results of this discussion:

1. The domain-calculus, in which the fundamental relation is that of part to whole, must be wholly separated from logic. For logic Euler's diagrams are only a lame analogy.

2. The extension of a concept does not consist of objects falling under the concept, in the way, e.g., that a wood consists of trees; it attaches to the concept and to this alone. The concept thus takes logical precedence of its extension.

3. We must keep separate from one another:

(a) the relation of an object (an individual) to the exten-
p. 456] sion of a concept when it falls under the concept (the *subter* relation);

(b) the relation between the extension of one concept and that of another when the first concept is subordinate to the second (the *sub* relation).

4. By means of a definition we can neither create an object with any properties we like, nor magically confer any properties we like on an empty name or symbol.

5. The questions whether a proper name stands for something, and whether a concept comprehends something under itself, must be kept separate. Proper names without any reference are illegitimate in science; empty concepts cannot be banished.

* It would take us too far here to explain more precisely the nature of the concept. I therefore refer to my address *Function und Begriff*, Pohle, Jena, 1891; to my paper *Ueber Begriff und Gegenstand* (*Vierteljahrsschrift für wissenschaftl. Philosophie*, XVI. 2); and to what I have said in my *Grundgesetze der Arithmetik* (Pohle, Jena, 1893), Introduction and §3.

WHAT IS A FUNCTION?

First published in *Festschrift* Ludwig Boltzmann *gewidmet zum sechzigsten Geburtstage* 20 *Februar* 1904 (Ambrosius Barth, Leipzig, 1904); pp. 656-666.

IT is even now not beyond all doubt what the word 'function'* stands for in Analysis, although it has been in continual use for a long time. In definitions, we find two expressions constantly recurring, sometimes in combination and sometimes separately: 'mathematical expression' and 'variable.' We also notice a fluctuating usage: the name 'function' is given sometimes to what determines the mode of dependence, or perhaps to the mode of dependence itself, and sometimes to the dependent variable.

In recent times the word 'variable' is predominant in the definitions. But this is itself very much in need of explanation. Any variation occurs in time. Consequently Analysis would have to deal with a process in time, since it takes variables into consideration. But in fact it has nothing to do with time; its applicability to occurrences in time is irrelevant. There are also applications of Analysis to geometry; and here time is left quite out of account. This is one of the main difficulties, one that we encounter again and again when once we try to get away from examples to the root of the matter. For as soon as we try to mention a variable, we shall hit upon something that varies in time and thus does not belong to pure Analysis. And yet it must be possible to point to a variable that does not involve something alien to arithmetic, if variables are objects of Analysis at all.

p. 657] If variation thus already raises a difficulty, we encounter a fresh one when we ask what varies. The answer one immediately gets is: a magnitude. Let us look for an example. We may call a rod a magnitude in respect of its being long. Any variation in the rod as regards its length, such as may result, e.g., from heating it, occurs in time; and neither rods nor lengths are objects of pure Analysis. This attempt to point to a variable magnitude within Analysis is a failure; and in just the same way, many others must

* Our discussion will be confined to functions of a single argument.

fail; for the magnitudes of lengths, surfaces, angles, masses, are none of them objects of arithmetic. Among all magnitudes, only numbers belong to arithmetic; and it is just because this science leaves wholly indefinite what magnitudes were measured in particular cases so as to get numbers, that it admits of the most various applications. Our question is, then: Are the variables of Analysis variable numbers? What else could they be, if they are to belong to Analysis at all? But why is it that people hardly ever say 'variable number' but on the other hand often say 'variable magnitude'? The latter expression sounds more acceptable than 'variable number'; for as regards that there arises the doubt: are there variable numbers? Surely every number retains its properties, without varying. 'Of course,' someone may say, '3 and π are obviously invariable numbers, constants; but there are also variable numbers. For example, when I say "the number that gives the length of this rod in millimetres" I am naming a number; and this is variable, because the rod does not always keep the same length; so by using this expression I have designated a variable number.' Let us compare this example with the following one. 'When I say "the King of this realm" I am designating a man. Ten years ago the King of this realm was an old man; at present the King of this realm is a young man. So by using this expression I have designated a man who was an old man and is now a young man.' There must be something wrong here. The expression 'the King of this realm' does not designate any man at all, if the time is not mentioned; as soon, however, as mention of a time is added, it can designate one man unambiguously; but then this p. 658] mention of a time is a necessary constituent of the expression, and we get a different expression if we mention a different time. Thus in our two sentences we just have not the same subject of predication. Similarly, the expression 'the number that gives the length of this rod in millimetres' does not designate any number at all if the time is not mentioned. If mention of a time is added, a number may thus be designated, e.g. 1,000; but then this is invariable. If a different time is mentioned, we get a different expression, which may thus also designate a different number, say 1,001. If we say 'Half an hour ago the number that gave the length of this rod in millimetres was a cube; at present the number that gives the length of this rod in millimetres is not a cube,' we just have not got the same subject of predication. The number 1,000 has not somehow swollen up to 1,001, but has been replaced by it. Or is the number 1,000 perhaps the same as the number 1,001, only with a different expression on its face? If anything varies, we have in succession different properties, states, in the same object. If it were not the same one, we should have no subject of which we could predicate variation. A rod grows longer through being heated; while this is going on, it remains the same one. If instead it were taken away and replaced by a longer one, we could not say it had grown longer. A man grows older; but if we could not nevertheless recognize him as the same man, we should have nothing of which we could predicate growing older. Let us apply this to number. What remains the same when a number varies? Nothing! Hence a number does *not* vary; for we have nothing of which we could predicate the variation. A cube never turns into a prime number; an irrational number never becomes rational.

Thus there are no variable numbers; and this is confirmed by the fact that we have no proper names for variable numbers. We failed in our attempt to use the expression 'the number that gives the length of this rod in millimetres' as a designation of a variable number. But do we not use 'x,' 'y,' 'z' to designate p. 659] variable numbers? This way of speaking is certainly employed; but these letters are not proper names of variable numbers in the way that '2' and '3' are proper names of constant numbers; for the numbers '2' and '3' differ in a specified way, but what is the difference between the variables that are said to be designated by 'x' and 'y'? We cannot say. We cannot specify what properties x has and what differing properties y has. If we associate anything with these letters at all, it is the same vague image for both of them. When apparent differences do show themselves, it is a matter of applications; but we are not here talking about these. Since we cannot conceive of each variable in its individual being, we cannot attach any proper names to variables.

Herr E. Czuber has attempted to avoid some of the difficulties I have mentioned.* In order to eliminate time, he defines the

* *Vorlesungen uber Differential- und Integralrechnung* (Teubner, Leipzig) 1, §2.

variable as an indefinite number. But are there indefinite numbers? Must numbers be divided into definite and indefinite? Are there indefinite men? Must not every object be definite? 'But is not the number n indefinite?' I am not acquainted with the number n. 'n' is not the proper name of any number, definite or indefinite. Nevertheless, we do sometimes say 'the number n.' How is this possible? Such an expression must be considered in a context. Let us take an example. 'If the number n is even, then $\cos n\pi = 1$.' Here only the whole has a sense, not the antecedent by itself nor the consequent by itself. The question whether the number n is even cannot be answered; no more can the question whether $\cos n\pi = 1$. For an answer to be given, 'n' would have to be the proper name of a number, and in that case this would necessarily be a definite one. We write the letter 'n' in order to achieve generality. This presupposes that, if we replace it by the name of a number, both antecedent and consequent receive a sense.

Of course we may speak of indefiniteness here; but here the p. 660] word 'indefinite' is not an adjective of 'number,' but ['indefinitely'] is an adverb, e.g., of the verb 'to indicate.'[A] We cannot say that 'n' designates an indefinite number, but we *can* say that it indicates numbers indefinitely. And so it is always when letters are used in arithmetic, except for the few cases (π, e, i) where they occur as proper names; but then they designate definite, invariable numbers. There are thus no indefinite numbers, and this attempt of Herr Czuber's is a failure.

The second deficiency that he tries to remedy is that we cannot conceive of any variable so as to distinguish it from others. He calls the totality of the values that a variable may assume, the range of the variable, and says: 'The variable x counts as having been defined when it can be determined as regards any assigned real number whether it belongs to the range or not.' It counts as having been defined; but *has* it? Since there are no indefinite numbers, it is impossible to define any indefinite number. The range is represented as distinctive for the variable; so with the same range we should have the same variable.

A The insertion is needed because in English, unlike German, adjectives mostly have no adverbial use.

Consequently in the equation '$y = x^2$' y would be the same variable as x if the range of x is that of positive numbers.

We must regard this attempt as having come to grief; in particular, the expression 'a variable assumes a value' is completely obscure. A variable is to be an indefinite number. Now how does an indefinite number set about assuming a number? for the value is obviously a number. Does, e.g., an indefinite man likewise assume a definite man? In other connexions, indeed, we say that an object assumes a property; here the number must play both parts; as an object it is called a variable or a variable magnitude, and as a property it is called a value. That is why people prefer the word 'magnitude' to the word 'number'; they have to deceive themselves about the fact that the variable magnitude and the value it is said to assume are essentially the same thing, that in this case we have *not* got an object assuming different properties in succession, and that therefore there can be no question of a variation.

p. 661] As regards variables our results are as follows. Variable magnitudes may certainly be admitted, but do not belong to pure Analysis. Variable numbers do not exist. The word 'variable' thus has no justification in pure Analysis.

Now how do we get from the variable to the function? This will probably be done always in essentially the same way; so we follow Herr Czuber's way of putting it. He writes (§ 3): 'If every value of the real variable x that belongs to its range has correlated with it a definite number y, then in general y also is defined as a variable, and is called *a function of the real variable x*. This relation is expressed by an equation of the form $y = f(x)$.'

It is at once noticeable that y is called a definite number, whereas on the other hand, being a variable, it would have to be an indefinite number. y is neither a definite nor an indefinite number; but the sign 'y' is attached incorrectly to a plurality of numbers, and then afterwards he talks as if there were only a single number. It would be simpler and clearer to state the matter as follows. 'With every number of an x-range there is correlated a number. I call the totality of these numbers the y-range.' Here we certainly have a y-range, but we have no y of which we could say that it was a function of the real variable x.

Now the delimitation of the range appears irrelevant to the question what the function essentially is. Why could we not at once take the range to be the totality of real numbers, or the totality of complex numbers, including real numbers? The heart of the matter really lies in quite a different place, viz. hidden in the word 'correlated.' Now how do I tell whether the number 5 is correlated with the number 4? The question is unanswerable unless it is somehow completed. And yet with Herr Czuber's explanation it looks as though it were already determined, for any two numbers, whether the first is correlated with the second or not. Fortunately Herr Czuber adds the p. 662] remark: 'The above definition involves no assertion as to the *law* of correlation, which is indicated in the most general way by the *characteristic f*; this can be set up in the most various ways.'

Correlation, then, takes place according to a law, and different laws of this sort can be thought of. In that case, the expression '*y* is a function of *x*' has no sense, unless it is completed by mentioning the law of correlation. This is a mistake in the definition. And surely the law, which this definition treats as not being given, is really the main thing. We notice that now variability has dropped entirely out of sight; instead, generality comes into view, for that is what the word 'law' indicates.

Distinctions between laws of correlation will go along with distinctions between functions; and these cannot any longer be regarded as quantitative. If we just think of algebraic functions, the logarithmic function, elliptic functions, we convince ourselves immediately that here it is a matter of qualitative differences; a further reason for not defining functions as variables. If they were variables, elliptic functions would be elliptic variables.

Our general way of expressing such a law of correlation is an equation, in which the letter '*y*' stands on the left side whereas on the right there appears a mathematical expression consisting of numerals, mathematical signs, and the letter '*x*,' e.g.:

$$'y = x^2 + 3x'$$

The function has indeed been defined as being such a mathematical expression. In recent times this concept has been found too narrow. However, this difficulty could easily be avoided by introducing new signs into the symbolic language of arithmetic. Another objection has more weight: viz. that a mathematical expression, as a group of signs, does not belong in arithmetic at all. The formalist theory, which regards signs as the subject-matter of this science, is one that I may well consider to be p. 663] definitively refuted by my criticism in the second volume of my *Grundgesetze der Arithmetik*. The distinction between sign and thing signified has not always been sharply made, so 'mathematical expression' (*expressio analytica*) has been half taken to mean also what the expression stands for. Now what does '$x^2 + 3x$' designate? Properly speaking, nothing at all; for the letter 'x' only indicates numbers, and does not designate them. If we replace 'x' by a numeral, we get an expression that designates a number, and so nothing new. Like 'x' itself, '$x^2 + 3x$' only indicates. This may be done for the sake of expressing generality, as in the sentences

$$'x^2 + 3x = x\,(x + 3)'$$
$$'\text{if } x > \text{o then } x^2 + 3x > \text{o.}'$$

But now what has become of the function? It looks as though we could not take it to be either the mathematical expression itself or what the expression stands for. And yet we have not gone very far off the right track. Each of the expressions 'sin o,' 'sin 1,' 'sin 2' stands for a particular number; but we have a common constituent '*sin*,' and here we find a designation for the essential peculiarity of the sine-function. This '*sin*' perhaps corresponds to the '*f*' that Herr Czuber says indicates a law; and the transition from '*f*' to '*sin*,' just like that from '*a*' to '2,' is a transition from a sign that indicates to one that designates. In that case '*sin*' would stand for a law. Of course that is not quite right. The law seems rather to be expressed in the equation '$y = \sin x$'; the symbol '*sin*' is only part of this, but the part that is distinctive for the essential peculiarity of the law. And surely we have here what we were looking for—the function. '*f*' too will then, strictly speaking, indicate a function. And here we come upon what distinguishes functions from numbers. '*Sin*' requires completion with a numeral, which, however, does not form part of the designation of the function. This holds good in general; the sign for a function is 'unsaturated'; it needs to be completed with a numeral, which we then call the argument-sign. We see this also with the root-sign, with the logarithm-sign. p. 664] The functional sign cannot occur on one side of an equation by itself, but only when completed by a sign that designates or indicates a number. Now what does such a complex stand for, consisting of a functional sign and a numeral, e.g. 'sin 1,' '$\sqrt{1}$,' 'log 1'? A number each time. We thus get numerical signs composed of two dissimilar parts, an 'unsaturated' part being completed by the other one.

This need of completion may be made apparent by empty brackets, e.g. 'sin ( )' or '( )^2 + 3. ( ).' This is perhaps the most appropriate notation, and the one best calculated to avoid the confusion that arises from regarding the argument-sign as part of the functional sign; but it will probably not meet with any acceptance.* A letter may also be employed for this purpose. If we choose 'ξ,' then 'sin ξ' and 'ξ^2 + 3.ξ' are functional signs. But in that case it must be laid down that the only thing 'ξ' does here is to show the places where the completing sign has to be inserted. It will be well not to employ this letter for any other purpose, and so, e.g., not instead of the 'x' in our examples that serves to express generality.

It is a defect of the ordinary symbolism for differential quotients that in it the letter 'x' has to serve both to show the places for the argument and to express generality, as in the equation:

$$\frac{d \cos \frac{x}{2}}{dx} = - \frac{1}{2} \sin \frac{x}{2}$$

From this there arises a difficulty. According to the general principles for the use of letters in arithmetic we should have to get a particular case of substituting a numeral for 'x.' But the expression

$$\frac{d \cos \frac{2}{2}}{d2}$$

* In any case it is meant only for the exceptional case where we want to symbolize a function in isolation. In 'sin 2,' '*sin*' by itself already symbolizes the function.

p. 665] is unintelligible, because we cannot recognize the function. We do not know whether it is

$$\cos\left(\ \right), \text{ or } \cos\frac{2}{(\ )}, \text{ or } \cos\frac{(\ )}{(\ )}.$$

So we are forced to use the clumsy notation

$$\left(\frac{d\cos\frac{x}{2}}{dx}\right)_{x=2}$$

But the greater disadvantage is that it is thus made more difficult to see the nature of the function.

The peculiarity of functional signs, which we here called 'unsaturatedness,' naturally has something answering to it in the functions themselves. They too may be called 'unsaturated,' and in this way we mark them out as fundamentally different from numbers. Of course this is no definition; but likewise none is here possible.* I must confine myself to hinting at what I have in mind by means of a metaphorical expression, and here I rely on my reader's agreeing to meet me half-way.

If a function is completed by a number so as to yield a number, the second is called the value of the function for the first as argument. People have got used to reading the equation '$y = f(x)$' as 'y is a function of x.' There are two mistakes here: first, rendering the *equals*-sign as a copula; secondly, confusing the function with its value for an argument. From these mistakes has arisen the opinion that the function is a number, although a variable or indefinite one. We have seen, on the contrary, that there are no such numbers at all, and that functions are fundamentally different from numbers.

The endeavour to be brief has introduced many inexact expressions into mathematical language, and these have reacted by obscuring thought and producing faulty definitions. Mathep. 666] matics ought properly to be a model of logical clarity. In actual fact there are perhaps no scientific works where you

* H. Hankel's definition, in his *Untersuchungen über die unendlich oft oszillirenden und unstetigen Functionen* (Universitatsprogramm. Tubingen 1870), §1, is useless, because of a vicious circle; it contains the expression '$f(x)$,' and this makes his definition presuppose the thing that is to be defined.

will find more wrong expressions, and consequently wrong thoughts, than in mathematical ones. Logical correctness should never be sacrificed to brevity of expression. It is therefore highly important to devise a mathematical language that combines the most rigorous accuracy with the greatest possible brevity. To this end a symbolic language would be best adapted, by means of which we could directly express thoughts in written or printed symbols without the intervention of spoken language.

NEGATION

First published in *Beiträge zur Philosophie des deutschen Idealismus*, vol. i (1919); pp. 143-57

A PROPOSITIONAL question (*Satzfrage*) contains a demand that we should either acknowledge the truth of a thought, or reject it as false. In order that we may meet this demand correctly, two things are requisite: first, the wording of the question must enable us to recognize without any doubt the thought that is referred to; secondly, this thought must not belong to fiction. p. 144] I always assume in what follows that these conditions are fulfilled. The answer to a question* is an assertion based upon a judgment; this is so equally whether the answer is affirmative or negative.

Here, however, a difficulty arises. If a thought has being by being true, then the expression 'false thought' is just as self-contradictory, as 'thought that has no being.' In that case the expression 'the thought: three is greater than five' is an empty one; and accordingly in science it must not be used at all—except between quotation-marks. In that case we may not say 'that three is greater than five is false'; for the grammatical subject is empty.

But can we not at least ask if something is true? In a question we can distinguish between the demand for a decision and the special content of the question, the point we are to decide. In what follows I shall call this special content simply the content of the question, or the sense of the corresponding interrogative sentence. Now has the interrogative sentence

'Is 3 greater than 5?'

a sense, if the being of a thought consists in its being true? If not, the question cannot have a thought as its content; and one is inclined to say that the interrogative sentence has no sense at all. But this surely comes about because we see the falsity at once.

* Here and in what follows I always mean a propositional question when I just write 'question.'

Has the interrogative sentence

$$\text{'Is } \left(\tfrac{21}{20}\right)^{100} \text{ greater than } {}^{10}\sqrt{10^{21}} \text{?'}$$

got a sense? If we had worked out that the answer must be affirmative, we could accept the interrogative sentence as making sense, for it would have a thought as its sense. But what if the answer had to be negative? In that case, on our supposition, we should have no thought that was the sense of the question. But surely the interrogative sentence must have some sense or other, if it is to contain a question at all. And are we not really asking for something in this sentence? May we not be wanting to get an answer to it? In that case, it depends on the answer whether we are to suppose that the question has a thought as its content. But it must be already possible to grasp the sense of the interrogative sentence before answering the question; for otherwise no answer would be possible at all. So that which we can grasp as the sense of the interrogative sentence before answering the question—and only this can properly be called the sense of the interrogative sentence—cannot be a thought, if the being of a thought consists in being true. 'But is it not a truth that the Sun is bigger than the Moon? And does not the being of a truth just consist in its being true? Must we not therefore recognize after all that the sense of the interrogative sentence:

"Is the Sun bigger than the Moon?"

is a truth, a thought whose being consists in its being true?' No! Truth cannot go along with the sense of an interrogative sentence; that would contradict the very nature of a question. The content of a question is that as to which we must decide. p. 145] Consequently truth cannot be counted as going along with the content of the question. When I raise the question whether the Sun is bigger than the Moon, I am seeing the sense of the interrogative sentence

'Is the Sun bigger than the Moon?'

Now if this sense were a thought whose being consisted in its being true, then I should at the same time see that this sense was true. Grasping the sense would at the same time be an act of judging; and the utterance of the interrogative sentence would at the same time be an assertion, and so an answer to the question. But in an interrogative sentence neither the truth nor the falsity of the sense may be asserted. Hence an interrogative sentence has not as its sense something whose being consists in its being true. The very nature of a question demands a separation between the acts of grasping a sense and of judging. And since the sense of an interrogative sentence is always also inherent in the assertoric sentence that gives an answer to the question, this separation must be carried out for assertoric sentences too. It is a matter of what we take the word 'thought' to mean. In any case, we need a short term for what can be the sense of an interrogative sentence. I call this a thought. If we use language this way, not all thoughts are true. The being of a thought thus does not consist in its being true. We must recognize that there are thoughts in this sense, since we use questions in scientific work; for the investigator must sometimes content himself with raising a question, until he is able to answer it. In raising the question he is grasping a thought. Thus I may also say: The investigator must sometimes content himself with grasping a thought. This is anyhow already a step towards the goal, even if it is not yet a judgment. There must, then, be thoughts, in the sense I have assigned to the word. Thoughts that perhaps turn out later on to be false have a justifiable use in science, and must not be treated as having no being. Consider indirect proof; here knowledge of the truth is attained precisely through our grasping a false thought. The teacher says 'Suppose a were not equal to b.' A beginner at once thinks 'What nonsense! I can see that a *is* equal to b'; he is confusing the senselessness of a sentence with the falsity of the thought expressed in it.

Of course we cannot infer anything from a false thought; but the false thought may be part of a true thought, from which something can be inferred. The thought contained in the sentence:

'If the accused was in Rome at the time of the deed, he did not commit the murder'*

may be acknowledged to be true by someone who does not know

* Here we must suppose that these words by themselves do not contain the thought in its entirety; that we must gather from the circumstances in which they are uttered how to supplement them so as to get a complete thought.

if the accused was in Rome at the time of the deed nor if he committed the murder. Of the two component thoughts contained in the whole, neither the antecedent nor the consequent is p. 146] being uttered assertively when the whole is presented as true. We have then only a single act of judgment, but three thoughts, viz. the whole thought, the antecedent, and the consequent. If one of the clauses were senseless, the whole would be senseless. From this we see what a difference it makes whether a sentence is senseless or whether it expresses a false thought. Now for thoughts consisting of an antecedent and a consequent there obtains the law that, without prejudice to the truth, the opposite of the antecedent may become the consequent and the opposite of the consequent, the antecedent. The English call this procedure *contraposition*. According to this law, we may pass from the proposition

'If $(21/20)^{100}$ is greater than $\sqrt[10]{10^{21}}$, then $(21/20)^{1000}$ is greater than 10^{21}'

to the proposition

'If $(21/20)^{1000}$ is not greater than 10^{21}, then $(21/20)^{100}$ is not greater than $\sqrt[10]{10^{21}}$'

And such transitions are important for indirect proofs, which would otherwise not be possible.

Now if the first complex thought has a true antecedent, viz. $(21/20)^{100}$ *is greater than* $\sqrt[10]{10^{21}}$, then the second complex thought has a false consequent, viz. $(21/20)^{100}$ *is not greater than* $\sqrt[10]{10^{21}}$. So anybody that admits the legitimacy of our transition from *modus ponens* to *modus tollens* must acknowledge that even a false thought has being; for otherwise either only the consequent would be left in the *modus ponens* or only the antecedent in the *modus tollens*; and one of these would likewise be suppressed as a nonentity.

The being of a thought may also be taken to lie in the possibility of different thinkers' grasping the thought as one and the same thought. In that case the fact that a thought had no being would consist in several thinkers' each associating with the sentence a sense of his own; this sense would in that case be a content of his particular consciousness, so that there would be no *common* sense that could be grasped by several people. Now is a false thought a thought that in this sense has no being? In that case investigators who had discussed among themselves whether bovine tuberculosis is communicable to men, and had finally agreed that such communicability did not exist, would be in the same position as people who had used in conversation the expression 'this rainbow,' and now came to see that they had not been designating anything by these words, since what each of them had had was a phenomenon of which he himself was the owner. The investigators would have to realize that they had been deceived by a false appearance; for the presupposition that could alone have made all their activity and talk reasonable would have turned out not to be fulfilled; they would not have been giving to the question that they discussed a sense common to all of them.

But it must be possible to put a question to which the true p. 147] answer is negative. The content of such a question is, in my terminology, a thought. It must be possible for several people who hear the same interrogative sentence to grasp the same sense and acknowledge the falsity of it. Trial by jury would assuredly be a silly arrangement if it could not be assumed that each of the jurymen could understand the question at issue in the same sense. So the sense of an interrogative sentence, even when the question has to be answered in the negative, is something that can be grasped by several people.

What else would follow if the truth of a thought consisted in the possibility of its being grasped by several people as one and the same thing, whereas a sentence that expressed something false had no sense common to several people?

If a thought is true and is a complex of thoughts of which one is false, then the whole thought could be grasped by several people as one and the same thing, but the false component thought could not. Such a case may occur. E.g. it may be that the following assertion is justifiably made before a jury: 'If the accused was in Rome at the time of the deed, he did not commit the murder'; and it may be false that the accused was in Rome at the time of the deed. In that case the jurymen could grasp the same thought when they heard the sentence 'If the accused was in Rome at the time of the deed, he did not commit the murder,' whereas each of them would associate a sense of his own with the *if*-clause. Is this possible? Can a thought that is present to all the jurymen as one and the same thing have a part that is not common to all of them? If the whole needs no owner, no part of it needs an owner.

So a false thought is not a thought that has no being—not even if we take 'being' to mean 'not needing an owner.' A false thought must be acknowledged, not indeed as true, but as sometimes indispensable: first, as the sense of an interrogative sentence; secondly, as part of a hypothetical thought-complex; thirdly, in negation. It must be possible to negate a false thought, and for this I need the thought; I cannot negate what is not there. And by negation I cannot transform something that needs me as its owner into something of which I am not the owner, and which can be grasped by several people as one and the same thing.

Now is negation of a thought to be regarded as dissolution of the thought into its component parts? By their negative verdict the jury can in no way alter the make-up of the thought that the question presented to them expresses. The thought is true or false quite independently of their giving a right or a wrong verdict in regard to it. And if it is false it is still a thought. If after the jury's verdict there is no thought at all, but only fragments of thought, then the same was already the case before the verdict; in what looked like a question, the jury were not presented with any thought at all, but only with fragments of thought; they had nothing to pass a verdict on.

Our act of judgment can in no way alter the make-up of a thought. We can only recognize what is there. A true thought p. 148] cannot be affected by our act of judgment. In the sentence that expresses the thought we can insert a 'not'; and the sentence we thus get does not contain a non-thought (as I have shown) but may be quite justifiably used as antecedent or consequent in a hypothetical sentence complex. Only, since it is false, it may not be uttered assertively. But this procedure does not touch the original thought in any way; it remains true as before.

Can we affect a false thought somehow by negating it? We cannot do this either; for a false thought is still a thought and may occur as a component part of a true thought. The sentence

'3 is greater than 5,'

uttered non-assertively, has a false sense; if we insert a 'not,' we get

'3 is not greater than 5,'

a sentence that may be uttered assertively. There is no trace here of a dissolution of the thought, a separation of its parts.

How, indeed, could a thought be dissolved? How could the interconnexion of its parts be split up? The world of thoughts has a model in the world of sentences, expressions, words, signs. To the structure of the thought there corresponds the compounding of words into a sentence; and here the order is in general not indifferent. To the dissolution or destruction of the thought there must accordingly correspond a tearing apart of the words, such as happens, e.g., if a sentence written on paper is cut up with scissors, so that on each scrap of paper there stands the expression for part of a thought. These scraps can then be shuffled at will or carried away by the wind; the connexion is dissolved, the original order can no longer be recognized. Is this what happens when we negate a thought? No! The thought would undoubtedly survive even this execution of it in effigy. What we do is to insert the word 'not,' and, apart from this, leave the word-order unaltered. The original wording can still be recognized; the order may not be altered at will. Is this dissolution, separation? Quite the reverse! it results in a firmly-built structure.

Consideration of the law *duplex negatio affirmat* makes it specially plain to see that negation has no separating or dissolving effect. I start with the sentence

'The Schneekoppe is higher than the Brocken.'

By putting in a 'not' I get:

'The Schneekoppe is not higher than the Brocken.'

(Both sentences are supposed to be uttered non-assertively.) A second negation would produce something like the sentence

'It is not true that the Schneekoppe is not higher than the Brocken.'

We already know that the first negation cannot effect any dis-solution of the thought; but all the same let us suppose for once

p. 149] that after the first negation we had only fragments of a thought. We should then have to suppose that the second negation could put these fragments together again. Negation would thus be like a sword that could heal on again the limbs it had cut off. But here the greatest care would be wanted. The parts of the thought have lost all connexion and inter-relation on account of its being negated the first time. So by carelessly employing the healing power of negation, we might easily get the sentence:

'The Brocken is higher than the Schneekoppe.'

No non-thought is turned into a thought by negation, just as no thought is turned into a non-thought.

A sentence with the word 'not' in its predicate may, like any other, express a thought that can be made into the content of a question; and this, like any propositional question, leaves open our decision as to the answer.

What then are these objects, which negation is supposed to separate? Not parts of sentences; equally, not parts of a thought. Things in the outside world? They do not bother about our negating. Mental images in the interior world of the person who negates? But then how does the juryman know which of his images he ought to separate in given circumstances? The question put before him does not indicate any to him. It may evoke images in him. But the images evoked in the jurymen's interior worlds are different; and in that case each juryman would perform his own act of separation in his own private world, and this would not be a verdict.

It thus appears impossible to state what really is dissolved, split up, or separated by the act of negation.

With the belief that negation has a dissolving or separating power there hangs together the view that a negative thought is less useful than an affirmative one. But still it cannot be regarded as wholly useless. Consider the inference:

'If the accused was not in Berlin at the time of the murder, he did not commit the murder; now the accused was not in Berlin at the time of the murder; therefore he did not commit the murder,' and compare it with the inference:

'If the accused was in Rome at the time of the murder, he did not commit the murder; now the accused was in Rome at the time of the murder; therefore he did not commit the murder.'

Both inferences proceed in the same form, and there is not the least ground in the nature of the case for our distinguishing between negative and affirmative premises when we are expressing the law of inference here involved. People speak of affirmative and negative judgments; even Kant does so. Translated into my terminology, this would be a distinction between affirmative and negative thoughts. For logic at any rate such a distinction is wholly unnecessary; its ground must be sought outside logic. I know of no logical principle whose verbal expression makes it p. 150] necessary, or even preferable, to use these terms.* In any science in which it is a question of conformity to laws, the thing that must always be asked is: What technical expressions are necessary, or at least useful, in order to give precise expression to the laws of this science? What does not stand this test cometh of evil.^A

What is more, it is by no means easy to state what is a negative judgment (thought). Consider the sentences 'Christ is immortal,' 'Christ lives for ever,' 'Christ is not immortal,' 'Christ is mortal,' 'Christ does not live for ever.' Now which of the thoughts we have here is affirmative, which negative?

We usually suppose that negation extends to the whole thought when 'not' is attached to the verb of the predicate. But sometimes the negative word grammatically forms part of the subject, as in the sentence 'no man lives to be more than a hundred.' A negation may occur anywhere in a sentence without making the thought indubitably negative. We see what tricky questions the expression 'negative judgment (thought)' may lead to. The result may be endless disputes, carried on with the greatest subtlety, and nevertheless essentially sterile. Accordingly I am in favour of

* Accordingly, in my essay *The Thought* (*Beiträge zur Philosophie des deutschen Idealismus*, Vol. i, p. 58) I likewise made no use of the expression 'negative thought.' The distinction between negative and affirmative thoughts would only have confused the matter. At no point would there have been occasion to assert something about affirmative thoughts, excluding negative ones, or to assert something about negative thoughts, excluding affirmative ones.

^A An apparent allusion to Matthew v. 37!

dropping the distinction between negative and affirmative judgments or thoughts until such time as we have a criterion enabling us to distinguish with certainty in any given case between a negative and an affirmative judgment. When we have such a criterion we shall also see what benefit may be expected from this distinction. For the present I still doubt whether this will be achieved. The criterion cannot be derived from language; for languages are unreliable on logical questions. It is indeed not the least of the logician's tasks to indicate the pitfalls laid by language in the way of the thinker.

After refuting errors, it may be useful to trace the sources from which they have flowed. One source, I think, in this case is the desire to give definitions of the concepts one means to employ. It is certainly praiseworthy to try to make clear to oneself as far as possible the sense one associates with a word. But here we must not forget that not everything can be defined. If we insist at any price on defining what is essentially indefinable, we readily fasten upon inessential accessories, and thus start the inquiry on a wrong track at the very outset. And this is certainly what has happened to many people, who have tried to explain what a judgment is p. 151] and so have hit upon compositeness.* The judgment is composed of parts that have a certain order, an interconnexion, stand in mutual relations; but for what whole do we not get this?

There is another mistake associated with this one: viz. the view that the judging subject sets up the connexion or order of the parts in the act of judging and thereby brings the judgment into

---

* We are probably best in accord with ordinary usage if we take a judgment to be an act of judging, as a leap is an act of leaping. Of course this leaves the kernel of the difficulty uncracked; it now lies in the word 'judging.' Judging, we may say, is acknowledging the truth of something; what is acknowledged to be true can only be a thought. The original kernel now seems to have cracked in two; one part of it lies in the word 'thought' and the other in the word 'true.' Here, for sure, we must stop. The impossibility of an infinite regress in definition is something we must be prepared for in advance.

If the judgment is an act, it happens at a certain time and thereafter belongs to the past. With an act there also belongs an agent, and we do not know the act completely if we do not know the agent. In that case, we cannot speak of a synthetic judgment in the usual sense. If we call it a synthetic judgment that through two points only one straight line passes, then we are taking 'judgment' to mean, not an act performed by a definite man at a definite time, but something timelessly true, even if its being true is not acknowledged by any human being. If we call this sort of thing a truth, then we may perhaps with advantage say 'synthetic truth' instead of 'synthetic judgment.' If we do nevertheless prefer the expression 'synthetic judgment,' we must leave out of consideration the sense of the verb 'to judge.'

existence. Here the act of grasping a thought and the acknowledgment of its truth are not kept separate. In many cases, of
course, one of these acts follows so directly upon the other that
they seem to fuse into one act; but not so in all cases. Years of
laborious investigations may come between grasping a thought
and acknowledging its truth. It is obvious that here the act of
judging did not make the thought or set its parts in order; for the
thought was already there. But even the act of grasping a thought
is not a production of the thought, is not an act of setting its parts
in order; for the thought was already true, and so was already
there with its parts in order, before it was grasped. A traveller
who crosses a mountain-range does not thereby make the
mountain-range; no more does the judging subject make a
thought by acknowledging its truth. If he did, the same thought
could not be acknowledged as true by one man yesterday and
another man to-day; indeed, the same man could not recognize
the same thought as true at different times—unless we supposed
that the existence of the thought was an intermittent one.

If someone thinks it within his power to produce by an act of
judgment that which, in judging, he acknowledges to be true,
by setting up an interconnexion, an order, among its parts;
then it is easy for him to credit himself also with the power of
destroying it. As destruction is opposed to construction, to
setting up order and interconnexion, so also negating seems to be
p. 152] opposed to judging; and people easily come to suppose
that the interconnexion is broken up by the act of negation just
as it is built up by the act of judgment. Thus judging and negating
look like a pair of polar opposites, which, being a pair, are co-
ordinate; a pair comparable, e.g., to oxidation and reduction in
chemistry. But when once we see that no interconnexion is set
up by our judging; that the parts of the thought were already in
their order before our judging; then everything appears in a
different light. It must be pointed out yet once more that to grasp
a thought is not yet to judge; that we may express a thought
in a sentence without asserting its truth; that a negative word may
be contained in the predicate of a sentence, in which case the sense
of this word is part of the sense of the sentence, part of the
thought; that by inserting a 'not' in the predicate of a sentence
meant to be uttered non-assertively, we get a sentence that

expresses a thought, as the original one did. If we call such a transition, from a thought to its opposite, negating the thought, then negating in this sense is not co-ordinate with judging, and may not be regarded as the polar opposite of judging; for what matters in judging is always the truth, whereas we may pass from a thought to its opposite without asking which is true. To exclude misunderstanding, let it be further observed that this transition occurs in the consciousness of a thinker, whereas the thoughts that are the *termini a quo* and *ad quem* of the transition were already in being before it occurred; so that this psychical event makes no difference to the make-up and the mutual relations of the thoughts.

Perhaps the act of negating, which maintains a questionable existence as the polar opposite of judging, is a chimerical construction, formed by a fusion of the act of judging with the negation that I have acknowledged as a possible component of a thought, and to which there corresponds in language the word 'not' as part of the predicate—a chimerical construction, because these parts are quite different in kind. The act of judging is a psychical process, and as such it needs a judging subject as its owner; negation on the other hand is part of a thought, and as such, like the thought itself, it needs no owner, must not be regarded as a content of a consciousness. And yet it is not quite incomprehensible how there can arise at least the illusion of such a chimerical construction. Language has no special word or syllable to express assertion; assertive force is supplied by the form of the assertoric sentence, which is specially well-marked in the predicate. On the other hand the word 'not' stands in intimate connexion with the predicate and may be regarded as part of it. Thus a connexion may seem to be formed between the word 'not' and the assertoric force in language that answers to the act of judging.

But it is a nuisance to distinguish between the two ways of negating. Really my only aim in introducing the polar opposite of judging was to accommodate myself to a way of thinking that is foreign to me. I now return to my previous way of p. 153] speaking. What I have just been designating as the polar opposite of judging I will now regard as a second way of judging —without thereby admitting that there is such a second way. I shall thus be comprising both polar opposites under the common term 'judging'; this may be done, for polar opposites certainly do belong together. The question will then have to be put as follows:

Are there two different ways of judging, of which one is used for the affirmative, and the other for the negative, answer to a question? Or is judging the same act in both cases? Does negating go along with judging? Or is negation part of the thought that underlies the act of judging? Does judging consist, even in the case of a negative answer to a question, in acknowledging the truth of a thought? In that case the thought will not be the one directly contained in the question, but the opposite of this.

Let the question run, e.g., as follows: 'Did the accused intentionally set fire to his house?' How can the answer take the form of an assertoric sentence, if it turns out to be negative? If there is a special way of judging for when we deny, we must correspondingly have a special form of assertion. I may, e.g., say in this case 'it is false that . . .' and lay it down that this must always have assertoric force attached to it. Thus the answer will run something like this: 'It is false that the accused intentionally set fire to his house.' If on the other hand there is only one way of judging, we shall say assertorically: 'The accused did not intentionally set fire to his house.' And here we shall be presenting as something true the opposite thought to the one expressed in the question. The word 'not' here belongs with the expression of this thought. I now refer back to the two inferences I compared together just now. The second premise of the first inference was the negative answer to the question 'was the accused in Berlin at the time of the murder?'—in fact, the answer that we fixed upon in case there is only one way of judging. The thought contained in this premise is contained in the *if*-clause of the first premise, but there it is uttered non-assertively. The second premise of the second inference was the affirmative answer to the question 'Was the accused in Rome at the time of the murder?' These inferences proceed on the same principle, which is in good agreement with the view that judging is the same act whether the answer to a question is affirmative or negative. If on the other hand we had to recognize a special way of judging for the negative case—and correspondingly, in the realm of words and sentences, a special form of assertion—the matter would be otherwise. The first premise of the first inference would run as before:

'If the accused was not in Berlin at the time of the murder, he did not commit the murder.'

Here we could not say 'If it is false that the accused was in Berlin at the time of the murder'; for we have laid it down that to the words 'it is false that' assertoric force must always be attached; but in acknowledging the truth of this first premise we are not p. 154] acknowledging the truth either of its antecedent or of its consequent. The second premise on the other hand must now run: 'It is false that the accused was in Berlin at the time of the murder'; for being a premise it must be uttered assertively. The inference now cannot be performed in the same way as before; for the thought in the second premise no longer coincides with the antecedent of the first premise; it is now the thought that the accused *was* in Berlin at the time of the murder. If nevertheless we want to allow that the inference is valid, we are thereby acknowledging that the second premise contains the thought that the accused was *not* in Berlin at the time of the murder. This involves separating negation from the act of judging, extracting it from the sense of 'it is false that . . .,' and uniting negation with the thought.

Thus the assumption of two different ways of judging must be rejected. But what hangs on this decision? It might perhaps be regarded as valueless, if it did not effect an economy of logical primitives and their expressions in language. On the assumption of two ways of judging we need:

1. affirmative assertion;
2. negative assertion, e.g. inseparably attached to the word 'false';
3. a negative word like 'not' in sentences uttered non-assertively.

If on the other hand we assume only a single way of judging, we only need:

1. assertion;
2. a negative word.

Such economy always shows that analysis has been pushed further, which leads to a clearer insight. There hangs together with this an economy as regards a principle of inference; with our decision we can make do with one where otherwise we need two. If we *can* make do with one way of judging, then we *must*; and in that case we cannot assign to one way of judging the function of setting up order and connexion, and to another, the function of dissolving this.

Thus for every thought there is a contradictory* thought; we acknowledge the falsity of a thought by admitting the truth of its contradictory. The sentence that expresses the contradictory thought is formed from the expression of the original thought by means of a negative word.

The negative word or syllable often seems to be more closely united to part of the sentence, e.g. the predicate. This may lead us to think that what is negated is the content, not of the whole sentence, but just of this part. We may call a man uncelebrated and thereby indicate the falsity of the thought that he is cele-
p. 155] brated. This may be regarded as the negative answer to the question 'is the man celebrated?'; and hence we may see that we are not here just negating the sense of a word. It is incorrect to say: 'Because the negative syllable is combined with part of the sentence, the sense of the whole sentence is not negated.' On the contrary: it is by combining the negative syllable with a part of the sentence that we do negate the content of the whole sentence. That is to say: in this way we get a sentence in which there is a thought contradicting the one in the original sentence.

I do not intend by this to dispute that negation is sometimes restricted just to a part of the whole thought.

If one thought contradicts another, then from a sentence whose sense is the one it is easy to construct a sentence expressing the other. Consequently the thought that contradicts another thought appears as made up of that thought and negation. (I do not mean by this, the act of denial.) But the words 'made up of,' 'consist of,' 'component,' 'part' may lead to our looking at it the wrong way. If we choose to speak of parts in this connexion, all the same these parts are not mutually independent in the way that we are elsewhere used to find when we have parts of a whole. The thought does not, by its make-up, stand in any need of

* We could also say 'an opposite thought.'

completion; it is self-sufficient. Negation on the other hand needs to be completed by a thought. The two components, if we choose to employ this expression, are quite different in kind and contribute quite differently towards the formation of the whole. One completes, the other is completed. And it is by this completion that the whole is kept together. To bring out in language the need for completion, we may write 'the negation of . . .,' where the blank after 'of' indicates where the completing expression is to be inserted. For the relation of completing, in the realm of thoughts and their parts, has something similar corresponding to it in the realm of sentences and their parts. (The preposition 'of' <*von*> followed by a substantive can also be replaced <in German> by the genitive of the substantive; this may as a rule be more idiomatic, but does not lend itself so well to the purpose of expressing the part that needs completion.) An example may make it even clearer what I have here in mind. The thought that contradicts the thought:

$$(21/20)^{100} \text{ is equal to } \sqrt[10]{10^{21}}$$

is the thought:

$$(21/20)^{100} \text{ is not equal to } \sqrt[10]{10^{21}}.$$

We may also put this as follows:

'The thought:

$$(21/20)^{100} \text{ is not equal to } \sqrt[10]{10^{21}}$$

is the negation of the thought:

$$(21/20)^{100} \text{ is equal to } \sqrt[10]{10^{21}}.'$$

p. 156] In the last expression (after the penultimate 'is') we can see how the thought is made up of a part that needs completion and a part that completes it. From now on I shall use the word 'negation' (except, e.g., within quotation marks) always with the definite article. The definite article '*the*' in the expression

'*the* negation of the thought that 3 is greater than 5'

shows that this expression is meant to designate a definite single thing. This single thing is in our case a thought. The definite article makes the whole expression into a singular name, a proxy for a proper name.

The negation of a thought is itself a thought, and can again be used to complete *the negation*.[B] If I use, in order to complete *the negation*,[B] the negation of the thought that $(\frac{21}{20})^{100}$ is equal to $^{10}\sqrt{10^{21}}$, what I get is:

the negation of the negation of the thought that $(\frac{21}{20})^{100}$ is equal to $^{10}\sqrt{10^{21}}$.

This is again a thought. Designations of thoughts with such a structure are got according to the pattern:

'the negation of the negation of *A*,'

where '*A*' takes the place of the designation of a thought. Such a designation is to be regarded as directly composed of the parts:

'the negation of ——'
and 'the negation of *A*.'

But it may also be regarded as made up of the parts:

'the negation of the negation of ——'
and: '*A*.'

Here I have first combined the middle part with the part that stands to the left of it and then combined the result with the part '*A*' that stands to the right of it; whereas originally the middle part was combined with '*A*,' and the designation so got, viz.

'the negation of *A*,'

was combined with what stood to the left of it

'the negation of ——.'

The two different ways of regarding the designation have answering to them two ways of regarding the structure of the thought designated.[C]

If we compare the designations:

'the negation of the negation of: $(\frac{21}{20})^{100}$ is equal to $^{10}\sqrt{10^{21}}$'
and 'the negation of the negation of: 5 is greater than 3'

[B] I.e. to complete the thought-component whose verbal expression is '*the negation (of)* . . .', so as to get a complete thought; just as, in the realm of language, we get a complete designation of a thought by inserting a designation of a thought in the blank of 'the negation of ——.' (The italics in the text are mine, not Frege's.)

[C] *Bezeichnenden* is here surely a misprint for *bezeichneten* or *zu bezeichnenden*.

we recognize a common constituent:

'the negation of the negation of ——':

p. 157] this designates a part common to the two thoughts—a thought-component that stands in need of completion. In each of our two cases, it is completed by means of a thought: in the first case, the thought that $\left(\frac{21}{20}\right)^{100}$ is equal to $\sqrt[10]{10^{21}}$; in the second case, the thought that 5 is greater than 3. The result of this completion is in either case a thought. This common component, which stands in need of completion, may be called double negation. This example shows how something that needs completion can be amalgamated with something that needs completion to form something that needs completion. Here we are presented with a singular case; we have something—the negation of . . .— amalgamated with itself. Here, of course, metaphors derived from the corporeal realm fail us; for a body cannot be amalgamated with itself so that the result is something different from it. But then neither do bodies need completion, in the sense I intend here. Congruent bodies *can* be put together; and in the realm of designations we have congruence in our present case. Now what corresponds to congruent designations is one and the same thing in the realm of designata.

Metaphorical expressions, if used cautiously, may after all help towards an elucidation. I compare that which needs completion to a wrapping, e.g. a coat, which cannot stand upright by itself; in order to do that, it must be wrapped round somebody. The man whom it is wrapped round may put on another wrapping, e.g. a cloak. The two wrappings unite to form a single wrapping. There are thus two possible ways of looking at the matter; we may say either that a man who already wore a coat was now dressed up in a second wrapping, a cloak, or, that his clothing consists of two wrappings—coat and cloak. These ways of looking at it have absolutely equal justification. The additional wrapping always combines with the one already there to form a new wrapping. Of course we must never forget in this connexion that dressing up and putting things together are processes in time, whereas what corresponds to this in the realm of thoughts is timeless.

If A is a thought not belonging to fiction, the negation of A likewise does not belong to fiction. In that case, of the two thoughts: A and the negation of A: there is always one and only one that is true. Likewise, of the two thoughts: the negation of A, and the negation of the negation of A: there is always one and only one that is true. Now the negation of A is either true or not true. In the first case, neither A nor the negation of the negation of A is true. In the second case, both A and the negation of the negation of A are true. Thus of the two thoughts: A, and the negation of the negation of A: either both are true or neither is. I may express this as follows:

Wrapping up a thought in double negation does not alter its truth-value.

TRANSLATION OF PARTS OF FREGE'S
GRUNDGESETZE DER ARITHMETIK
Selections from Volume I
PREFACE

. . . . \. .

THE ideal of a strictly scientific method in mathematics, which I have tried to realize here, and which perhaps might be named after Euclid, I should like to describe in the following way.

It cannot be required that we should prove everything, because that is impossible; but we can demand that all propositions used without proof should be expressly mentioned as such, so that we can see distinctly what the whole construction rests upon. We should, accordingly, strive to diminish the number of these fundamental laws as much as possible, by proving everything that can be proved. Furthermore I demand—and in this I go beyond Euclid—that all the methods of inference used must be specified in advance. Otherwise it is impossible to ensure satisfying the first demand.

This ideal I believe I have attained in essentials; only in a few points could one possibly be more exacting. In order to secure more flexibility and not fall into excessive prolixity, I have taken the liberty of making tacit use of the interchangeability of the sub-clauses (conditions) and of the possibility of amalgamating identical sub-clauses;[A] and I have not reduced the modes of inference to the smallest possible number. Those who have read my *Begriffsschrift* will be able to gather from it that even in this respect it would be possible to satisfy the severest demands, but likewise that this would involve a considerable increase in volume.

I believe that, apart from this, the only objections that could vii] justly be raised against this book do not concern rigour but only the choice of the course of proofs and of the intermediate steps in them. Often there are several modes of proof possible; I have not tried to follow all of them out, and thus it is

A Frege means the possibility of passing from 'if *A*, then, if *B*, then *Γ*' to 'if *B*, then if *A*, then *Γ*,' and again from 'if *A* then, if *A*, then *B*' to 'if *A*, then *B*.'

possible—even probable—that I have not always chosen the shortest. But if anybody has any fault to find in this regard, let him do better himself. Other matters will be disputable. Some might have preferred to increase the number of permissible modes of inference and thereby to attain greater flexibility and brevity. But we have to stop somewhere, if my ideal is approved of at all; and wherever we stop, people will always be able to say: 'It would have been better to allow still more modes of inference.'

Since there are no gaps in the chains of inference, each axiom, assumption, hypothesis, or whatever you like to call it, upon which a proof is founded, is brought to light; and so we gain a basis for deciding the epistemological nature of the law that is proved. It has often been said that arithmetic is only a more highly developed logic; but that remains disputable as long as the proofs contain steps that are not performed according to acknowledged logical laws, but seem to rest on intuitive knowledge. Only when these are resolved into simple logical steps can we be sure that arithmetic is founded solely upon logic. I have gathered together everything that can make it easier to decide whether the chains of inference are convincing and the buttresses firm. If any one perchance finds anything faulty, he must be able to indicate exactly where, to his thinking, the mistake lies—whether in the fundamental laws, in the definitions, in the rules, or in their application at a definite place. If we find everything correct, we thus know the exact bases upon which each single theorem is founded. A dispute can only arise, so far as I can see, because of my fundamental law about 'ranges of values,'[B] which perhaps has not yet been specifically expressed by logicians, though it is in their minds when, e.g., they speak of extensions of concepts. I hold that it is purely logical. In any case the place is indicated where the decision has to be made.

My purpose requires many deviations from what is usual in mathematics. The requirements with regard to the rigour of proofs inevitably entail greater length. Whoever does not bear this in mind will often be surprised at the roundabout way in

[B] This axiom is numbered V on pp. 36 and 240 of Vol. I (1893) of the *Grundgesetze* and expresses that an equality of ranges both implies and is implied by the statement that an equation between functions holds generally. It first appeared on page 10 of Frege's lecture, *Function und Begriff* (Jena, 1891). Cf. p. 253 of Vol. II of the *Grundgesetze* (1903)

which a proposition is here proved, whereas he believes he can grasp the proof directly by a single act of understanding. This will surprise us especially if we compare the work of Dedekind, *Was sind und was sollen die Zahlen?*[c] which is the most thorough work on the foundation of arithmetic that I have lately seen. VIII] In a much smaller compass it follows the laws of arithmetic much farther than I do here. This brevity is only arrived at, to be sure, because much is not really proved at all. Dedekind often says only that the proof follows from such-and-such theorems; he uses little dots, as in the symbol $M(A, B, C, \ldots)$;[D] nowhere is there a statement of the logical or other laws on which he builds, and, even if there were, we could not possibly find out whether really no others were used—for to make that possible the proof must be not merely indicated but completely carried out. Dedekind also is of opinion that the theory of number is a part of logic; but his work hardly goes to strengthen this opinion, because the expressions 'system' and 'a thing belongs to a thing' used by him are not usual in logic and are not reduced to accepted logical notions. I do not say this as a reproach, for his method may have been the most serviceable to him for his purpose; I only say it in order to make my intentions clear by the contrast. The length of a proof is not to be measured by the yard. It is easy to make a proof appear short on paper by omitting many connecting links in the chain of inference and just indicating many points. Generally we are satisfied if every step in the proof is obviously correct; and we may well be so if we just want to convince someone as to the truth of the theorem to be proved. If we wish to bring about an insight into the nature of this obviousness this method does not suffice, but we must put down all the intermediate stages of reasoning, in order that the full light of consciousness may fall upon them. As a rule mathematicians are only interested in the content of a theorem and in the fact that it is to be proved. The novelty of this book does not lie in the content of the theorems, but in the development of the proofs and the foundations on which they are based. That this altogether different point of view

---

[c] English translation on pp. 29–115 of Dedekind's *Essays on the Theory of Numbers* (Chicago and London, 1901).

[D] Cf., e.g., paragraph 8 on p. 47 of the above translation.

needs a quite different treatment ought not to appear strange. If one of our theorems is deduced in the usual way, it will be easy to overlook a proposition which does not appear necessary for the proof. If my proof is carefully followed in thought, the indispensability of this proposition will, I believe, be seen, unless an altogether different mode of procedure is adopted. Thus perhaps you find here and there in our theorems conditions that appear at first to be unnecessary; but these nevertheless turn out to be necessary, or at least to admit of removal only by means of a proposition that must be specially proved.

With this book I accomplish an object which I had in view in my *Begriffsschrift* of 1879 and which I announced in my ix] *Grundlagen der Arithmetik*.* I am here trying to prove the opinion on the concept of number that I expressed in the book last mentioned. The fundamental part of my results is there expressed in § 46 by saying that assignment of a number involves an assertion about a concept; and upon this my present work is founded. If anybody is of another opinion let him try to construct symbolically a valid and usable exposition of his view, and he will see that it does not work. In language, it is true, the state of affairs is not so obvious, but if we look into the matter closely we find that here, too, assigning a number always goes along with naming a concept, not a group, an aggregate or such-like things; and that if a group or aggregate is named, it is always determined by a concept, that is to say, by the properties an object must have in order to belong to the group, while that which makes the group a group or the system a system—the mutual relations of members—is altogether irrelevant as regards the number of members.

The reason why the accomplishment appears so long after the programme is to be found in part in essential changes of my ideography, which have forced me to discard a manuscript that was almost completed. These improvements may be mentioned here briefly. The fundamental signs employed in my *Begriffsschrift* have, with one exception, been used again here Instead of the three parallel lines I have chosen the ordinary sign of equality because I convinced myself that it is used in arithmetic

---

* Cf. the Introduction and §§ 90 and 91 of my *Grundlagen der Arithmetik*, Breslau 1884.

to stand for the very thing that I wish to symbolize. In fact, I use the expression 'equal' to stand for the same as 'coinciding or identical with,' and this is just how the sign of equality is actually used in arithmetic. The objection which might perhaps be raised against this rests on an inadequate distinction between sign and thing signified. It is true that in the equation $2^2 = 2 + 2$ the sign on the left is different from the one on the right, but both signs designate or stand for the same number.* To the old fundamental signs two more have been added: The 'smooth breathing' (*spiritus lenis*) which serves towards designating the 'range of values' of a function, and a sign which is meant to take the place of the definite article of ordinary language. The introduction of the ranges of functions is an important advance which makes possible a far greater flexibility. The former derivative signs can now be replaced by other, simpler, ones, though the definitions of a relation's being many-one,[E] of following in a series, and of a projection (*Abbildung*),[F] are essentially the same as those which I have given partly in my *Begriffsschrift* and partly in my *Grundlagen der Arithmetik*. But x] the ranges have also a great fundamental importance: in fact I even define number itself as the extension of a concept, and extensions of concepts are, according to my definitions, ranges. So we just cannot do without ranges. The old fundamental signs, which reappear outwardly unchanged and whose algorithm has also hardly changed, have nevertheless been supplied with other explanations. The former 'content-stroke' (*Inhaltsstrich*) reappears as a horizontal (*Wagerechter*). These are consequences of an energetic development of my logical views. Formerly, I distinguished two elements in that which takes the external form of an assertoric sentence: (*a*) the acknowledgment of truth; (*b*) the content which is acknowledged to be true. The content I called the 'possible content of a judgment.' This has now

---

* I also say: the sense of the right-hand sign is different from that of the left-hand sign, but the reference is the same (*Zeitschr. für Philos. und philos. Kritik*, Vol. 100, 1892, pp. 25–50).

E Frege's '*eindeutig*,' as a predicate of relations, corresponds to 'many-one' in *Principia Mathematica*. If both a relation and its converse are *eindeutig*, many-one, then the relation is one-one—*beiderseits eindeutig* in Frege's terminology.

F If a many-one relation correlates to each member of the class Γ some member or other of the class Δ, then Frege says the relation *projects* (*abbildet*) the class-concept of the class Γ upon the class-concept of the class Δ. Cf. *Grundgesetze*, Vol. I, pp. 56–7.

split up into what I call 'thought' and 'truth value'; a consequence of the distinction between the sense and reference of a sign. In this case the sense of the sentence is the thought and its reference is the truth-value. Besides this, there is the acknowledgment that the truth-value is the True. (I distinguish two truth-values: the True and the False.) I have provided more thorough-going reasons for my view in my above-mentioned essay 'On Sense and Reference.' Here I may just say that only thus can *oratio obliqua* be rightly understood. The thought which is otherwise the sense of a sentence becomes, in *oratio obliqua*, its reference. How much more simple and distinct everything becomes by the introduction of truth-values can only be seen by an exhaustive examination of this book. These advantages alone put a great weight into the balance in favour of my view, which perhaps may seem strange at first sight. Also the essence of the function as opposed to the object is shown by means of sharper criteria than in my *Begriffsschrift*. From this results further the distinction between functions of the first and the second level. As I have shown in my essay *Function und Begriff* (Jena, 1891), concepts and relations are functions in my extended meaning of the word; and so we have to distinguish first-level and second-level concepts, equal-levelled and unequal-levelled relations.

From this it will be seen that the years have not passed in vain since the appearance of my *Begriffsschrift* and *Grundlagen*; they have brought my work to maturity. But just that which I recognize as an important advance forms, as I cannot help seeing, a great obstacle in the way of the circulation and effectiveness of my book. And the strict avoidance of gaps in the chain of conclusions, which to my way of thinking is not its least value, will win me, I am afraid, little gratitude. I have got farther away from xi] the traditional ideas and by so doing have given an appearance of paradox to my views. An expression encountered here and there on rapidly turning over these pages may easily appear strange and produce a prejudice against me. I myself can judge in a way what opposition my innovations will be met with because I have had to overcome something similar in myself. For it was not at random or because of the desire for innovation that I arrived at them; I was forced into them by the nature of the case.

With this I arrive at the second reason for my delay: the discouragement which at times came over me because of the cool reception, or rather the lack of reception, accorded by mathematicians,* to my works mentioned above and the opposing currents of scientific thought against which my book would have to fight. Even the first impression must frighten people away: unfamiliar signs, pages of nothing but strange-looking formulas. It is for that reason that I turned at times toward other subjects. But I could not keep the results of my thinking, which seemed valuable to me myself, locked up in my desk for any length of time; and the labour I had spent always required renewed labour that it might not be in vain. So the subject did not let go its hold upon me. In a case like the present one, when the value of a book cannot be recognized by a hasty perusal, criticism ought to be a help. But criticism is generally too badly repaid. A critic can never hope to get paid in cash for the pains which the thorough study of this book will cost him. The only remaining hope is that somebody may have beforehand sufficient confidence in the matter to expect that the mental profit will be sufficient recompense, and that he will then publish the results of his searching examination. It is not as if only a laudatory review would satisfy me; quite the contrary. I would far rather have an attack based on a thorough acquaintance with the subject than be praised in general terms which do not touch the root of the matter. . . .

xii] I must give up hope of securing as readers all those mathematicians who, when they come across logical expressions like 'concept,' 'relation,' 'judgment,' think: *Metaphysica sunt, non leguntur*; and those philosophers who at the sight of a formula call out: *Mathematica sunt, non leguntur*. The number of these people cannot be very small. Perhaps also the number of mathematicians who trouble themselves about the foundation of their science is not great, and even those who do often seem in a great hurry to get past the foundations. And I hardly dare hope that my reasons for laborious rigour and consequent lengthi- xiii] ness will convince many of them. As we know, what is

---

* In vain do we seek a notice of my *Grundlagen der Arithmetik* in the *Jahrbuch über die Fortschritte der Mathematik*. Investigators in the same domain, Dedekind, Otto Stolz, and von Helmholtz, do not seem to know my works. Nor does Kronecker mention them in his essay on the concept of number.

long established has great power over the minds of men. If I compare arithmetic with a tree which develops at the top into a multitude of methods and theorems while the root pushes downward, it seems to me that the growth of the root is, at least in Germany, rather weak. Even in a work which might be classed among those dealing with foundations, the *Algebra der Logik* of E. Schröder, the top-growth soon predominates and, even before a great depth has been reached, causes a bending upward and a development into methods and theorems.

The widespread inclination to recognize only what can be perceived by the senses as existing is also unfavourable for my book. It is sought to deny, or at least to overlook, what cannot be thus perceived. Now the objects of arithmetic, that is to say numbers, are of a kind which cannot be thus perceived. How are we to deal with them? Very simply; the signs used for the numbers are explained to be the numbers themselves. Then in the signs we have something visible, and that is the chief thing. No doubt the signs have altogether different properties from the numbers themselves, but what does that matter? We simply ascribe to them the desired properties by means of what we call definitions. How on earth there can be a definition where there is no question about connexions between sign and thing signified by it is a puzzle. We merge the sign and what it signifies as far as possible, without making any distinction between them; and according to our present requirement, we can either assert the existence of the result by referring to its tangibility,* or bring into prominence the real properties of numbers. Sometimes these number signs are, it seems, regarded as chessmen and the so-called definitions as rules of the game. The sign then does not signify anything, but is itself the subject-matter. It is true that in this one little thing is overlooked; viz. that we express a thought by $3^2 + 4^2 = 5^2$, while a position of chessmen does not express anything. Where people are satisfied with such superficialities, there is, of course, no basis for a deeper understanding.

Here it is of importance to make clear what definition is and what we can reach by means of it. It is, it seems, often

* Cf. E. Heine, 'Die Elemente der Functionslehre,' Crelle's *Journal für Math.*, Vol. LXXIV, p. 173: 'As regards definition I adopt a purely formalistic point of view: I give the name *numbers* to certain tangible signs, so that the existence of these numbers is thus unquestionable.'

credited with a creative power; but really all there is to definition is that something is brought out, precisely limited and given a name. The geographer does not create a sea when he draws border lines and says: The part of the surface of the ocean delimited by these lines, I am going to call the Yellow Sea; and no more can the mathematician really create anything by his act of definition. Nor can we by a mere definition magically give to a thing a property which it has not got, apart from the property of now being called by whatever name one has given XIV] it. But that an oval drawn on paper with pen and ink should acquire by definition the property that, when it is added to one, one is the result, I can only regard as a scientific superstition.

One might just as well make a lazy pupil diligent by a mere definition. Confusion easily arises here through our not making a sufficient distinction between concept and object. If we say: 'A square is a rectangle in which the adjacent sides are equal,' we define the concept *square* by specifying what properties something must have in order to fall under this concept. I call these properties 'marks' of the concept. But it must be carefully noted that these marks of the concept are not properties of the concept. The concept *square* is not a rectangle; only the objects which fall under this concept are rectangles; similarly the concept *black cloth* is neither black nor a cloth. Whether such objects exist is not immediately known by means of their definitions. Now, for instance, suppose we try to define the number zero by saying: 'It is something which when added to one gives the result one.' With that we have defined a concept by stating what property an object must have to fall under the concept. But this property is not a property of the concept defined. It seems that people often imagine that we have created by our definition something which when added to one gives one. This is a delusion. Neither has the concept defined got this property, nor is the definition a guarantee that the concept is realized. That must first of all be a matter for investigation. Only when we have proved that there exists one object and one only with the required property are we in a position to give this object the proper name 'zero.' To create zero is consequently impossible. I have already repeatedly explained this but, as it seems, without result.

From the prevailing logic I cannot hope for approval of the

distinction that I make between the mark of a concept and the property of an object,* for it seems to be thoroughly infected by psychology. If people consider, instead of things themselves, only subjective representations of them, only their own mental images —then all the more delicate distinctions in the things themselves are naturally lost, and others appear instead which are logically quite worthless.***G

xxiv] Let us now see how the finer distinctions in the subject-matter become obliterated in psychological logic. This has already been referred to above when we spoke of mark and property. With this is connected the distinction between object and concept emphasized by myself, and that between first-level and second-level concepts. These distinctions are, of course, indiscernible to the psychological logician; with such logicians xxv] everything is just idea. They have no right conception of those judgments which we express by 'there is.' This existence is confused by Erdmann† with actuality, which, as we have seen, is not clearly distinguished from objectivity. Of what thing do we assert that it is actual when we say that there are square roots of 4? Is it 2 or −2? But neither the one nor the other is named here in any way. And if I were to say that the number 2 acts or is active or actual, it would be false and quite different from what I mean by the sentence 'there are square roots of 4.' The confusion here under consideration is nearly the grossest possible; for it is not one between concepts of the same level, but a concept of the first level is confused with one of the second level. This is characteristic of the obtuseness of psychological logic. When we have arrived at a somewhat broader standpoint we may be surprised that such a mistake could be made by a professional logician; but we must have grasped the distinction between concepts of the first and second level before we can estimate the magnitude of this mistake, and psychological logic cannot do that. Here what most stands in the way of psychological logic is that its exponents have such a high opinion of psychological profundity, which is, after all, nothing but a psychological falsification of logic. And that is how our thick

---

* In the Logik of Benno Erdmann I find no trace of this important distinction.
† Op. cit., Vol. I, p. 311.

G pp. xv-xxiv here omitted in translation.

books of logic came to be; they are puffed out with unhealthy psychological fat which conceals all finer forms. Thus a fruitful collaboration of mathematicians and logicians is made impossible. While the mathematician defines objects, concepts, and relations, the psychological logician watches the becoming and changing of ideas, and at bottom the mathematicians' way of defining must appear to him just silly, because it does not reproduce the essence of ideation. He looks into his psychological peepshow and says to the mathematician: 'I cannot see anything at all of what you are defining.' And the mathematician can only reply: 'No wonder, for it is not where you are looking for it.'

This may be enough to throw a clearer light on my logical standpoint, by means of a contrast. This seems to me poles apart from psychological logic so that there is no prospect of my having at present any influence through my book upon psychological logic. It seems to me that the tree planted by me would have to lift an enormous weight of stone in order to gain room and light for itself. Nevertheless I should not like to give up all hope that my book may later on help to overthrow psychological logic. The notice that mathematicians cannot fail to take of my book will work to this end, and thus logicians will be compelled to come to terms with it. And I believe that I may expect some xxvi] help from mathematicians; for they have at bottom a common cause with me against the psychological logicians. As soon as mathematicians condescend to occupy themselves seriously with my book, if only in order to refute it, I believe I have won. For the whole of the second part is really a test of my logical convictions. It is improbable that such an edifice could be erected upon an unsound base. Those who have other convictions have only to try to erect a similar construction upon them, and they will soon be convinced that it is not possible, or at least is not easy. As a proof of the contrary, I can only admit the production by some one of an actual demonstration that upon other fundamental convictions a better and more durable edifice can be erected, or the demonstration by some one that my premises lead to manifestly false conclusions. But nobody will be able to do that. May my book then, even though it comes rather late, contribute to a revival of logic.

INTRODUCTION

In my *Grundlagen der Arithmetik* (1884) I tried to make it seem probable that arithmetic is a branch of logic and need not borrow any ground of proof whatever from experience or intuition. The actual demonstration of my thesis is carried out in my *Grundgesetze* [1893 and 1903] in the deduction of the simplest laws of numbers by logical means alone. But to make this proof convincing, considerably higher claims must be made for deduction than is usual in arithmetic.* A set of a few methods of deduction has to be fixed beforehand, and no step may be taken which is not in accordance with them. Consequently, when passing over to a new judgment we must not be satisfied, as mathematicians seem nearly always to have been hitherto, with saying that the new judgment is evidently correct, but we must analyse this transition into the simple logical steps of which it is composed—and often there are not a few of these simple steps. No hypothesis can thus remain unnoticed. Every axiom which is needed must be discovered, and it is just the hypotheses which are made tacitly and without clear consciousness that hinder our insight into the epistemological nature of a law.

In order that such an undertaking should succeed the concepts which we need must naturally be conceived distinctly. This is especially true as regards what mathematicians want to designate by the word 'set' (*Menge*). It seems that Dedekind, in his book *Was sind und was sollen die Zahlen?*H of 1888, uses the word 'system' for the same purpose. But in spite of the exposition which appeared four years earlier in my *Grundlagen*, a clear insight into the essence of the matter is not to be found in Dedekind's work, though he often gets near the mark. This is the case in the sentence:† 'Such a system *S* is completely determined if, as regards each thing, it is determinate whether it is an element of *S* or not. Hence the system *S* is the same as the p. 2] system *T* (in symbols *S* = *T*) if every element of *S* is also an element of *T* and every element of *T* is also an element of *S*.' In other passages, on the other hand, Dedekind strays from the

* *Grundlagen*, pp. 102–104. † Ibid., p. 45.

H English translation under the title *Essays on the Theory of Numbers*, Chicago and London, 1901. See especially p. 45.

point. For instance:* 'It very frequently happens that for some reason different things *a*, *b*, *c* . . . can be considered from a common point of view; . . . can be put together in the mind; and we then say that they form a *system S.*' Here the correct idea is suggested in the words 'common point of view'; but the 'considering,' 'putting together in the mind,' is not an objective characteristic. In whose mind, may I ask? If they are put together in one mind and not in another, do they then form a system? What is to be put together in my mind must doubtless be in my mind. Then do things outside myself not form systems? Is a system a subjective formation in each single mind? Is then the constellation Orion a system? And what are its elements? The stars, the molecules, or the atoms? The following sentence† is remarkable: 'For uniformity of expression it is advantageous to admit the special case that a system *S* is composed of a *single* (one and only one) element *a*: the thing *a* is an element of *S*, but every thing different from *a* is not an element of *S*.' This is afterwards‡ understood in such a way that every element *s* of a system *S* can be itself regarded as a system. Since in this case element and system coincide, it is here quite clear that, according to Dedekind, the elements are the proper constituents of a system. Ernst Schröder in his lectures on the algebra of logic§ goes a step in advance of Dedekind in drawing attention to the connexion of his systems with concepts, which Dedekind seems to have overlooked. Indeed, what Dedekind really means when he calls a system a 'part' of a system is that a concept is subordinated to a concept or an object falls under a concept. Neither Dedekind nor Schröder distinguish between these cases because of a mistaken view that is common to them both. In fact Schröder also, at bottom, considers the elements to be what really make up his *class*. An empty class should not occur with Schröder any more than an empty system with Dedekind. But the need arising from

---

* Ibid.   † Ibid.   ‡ Ibid., p. 46.
   § *Vorlesungen über die Algebra der Logik (exakte Logik)*, Vol. I, Leipsic, 1890, p. 253. [This reference of Frege seems wrong and it should perhaps rather be to such a page as p. 100. Cf. also Frege's later critical study: 'Kritische Beleuchtung einiger Punkte in E. Schröders 'Vorlesungen über die Algebra der Logik,' *Archiv für systematische Philosophie* Vol. I, 1895, pp. 433–456.]
   ‖ Ibid., p. 46.

the nature of the case makes itself felt in a different way with each writer. Dedekind goes on:* 'On the other hand, we shall here for certain reasons wholly exclude the empty system, which contains no element at all; although for other investigations it may be convenient to invent (*erdichten*) such a system.' Thus such an invention is permitted; only for certain reasons does he p. 3] abstain from it. Schröder ventures to invent an empty class. Apparently then both agree with many mathematicians in holding that we may invent anything we please that does not exist—is, in fact, unthinkable; for if it is the elements that form a system, then the system is removed at the same time as the elements. On the questions where the limits of this licence lie, and whether indeed there are any such limits, we are not likely to find much clearness and agreement—and yet the correctness of a proof may depend on such questions. I believe I have settled them in a way that is final for all intelligent persons, in my *Grundlagen*† and in my lecture *Ueber formale Theorien der Arithmetik*.‡ Schröder invents his null-class and thus gets entangled in great difficulties.§ We do not find, then, a clear insight into the matter with either Schröder or Dedekind; but still the true state of affairs makes itself apparent whenever a system has to be specified. Dedekind then brings forward properties which a thing must have in order to belong to a system, i.e. he defines a concept by its marks.|| Now if a concept is constituted by its marks and not by the objects falling under the concept, there are no difficulties or objections to be urged against an empty concept. Of course in this case an object can never also be a concept, and a concept under which only one object falls must not be confused with this object. Thus we are finally left with the result that the mention of a number involves an assertion about a concept.¶ I

* Ibid., pp. 45–46.
† pp. 104–108.
‡ *Sitzungsberichte der Jenaischen Gesellschaft fur Medicin und Naturwissenschaft*, July 17, 1885.
§ Cf. E. G. Husserl, *Göttinger gelehrte Anzeigen*, 1891, No. 7, p. 272, where, however, the difficulties are not solved.
|| On *concept, object, property*, and *marks* cf. my *Grundlagen*, pp. 48–50, 60–61, 64–65, and my essay *Ueber Begriff und Gegenstand*, *Vierteljahrsschrift für wissenschaftliche Philosophie*, Vol. XVI, 1892, pp. 192–205.
¶ See *Grundlagen*, pp. 59–60.

have traced back number to the relation of similarity[1] (*Gleichzah-ligkeit*) and similarity to many-one correlation (*eindeutige Zuord-nung*). About 'correlation' much the same holds as about the word 'set.' Nowadays both words are often used in mathematics, and very often there is lacking a deeper insight into what they are intended to mean. If my opinion is correct that arithmetic is a branch of pure logic, then a purely logical expression has to be chosen for 'correlation.' I choose the word 'relation.' Concept and relation are the foundation stones upon which I erect my structure.

But even when concepts have been grasped quite precisely, it would be difficult—almost impossible in fact—to satisfy the demands we must here make of proof, without some special device. Now such a device is my ideography (*Begriffsschrift*), the explanation of which will be my first task. The following p. 4] remark may be made before we proceed. It is not possible to give a regular definition of everything; for it must be our en-deavour to go back to what is logically simple and as such can-not properly be defined. I must then be satisfied with indicating by hints what I mean. Above all I must strive to be understood, and therefore I will try to develop the subject gradually and will not at first attempt full generality and a final expression.

The frequent use made of quotation marks may cause surprise. I use them to distinguish the cases where I speak about the sign itself from those where I speak about what it stands for. Pedantic as this may appear, I think it necessary. It is remarkable how an inexact mode of speaking or writing, which perhaps was originally employed only for greater convenience or brevity and with full consciousness of its inaccuracy, may end in a confusion of thought, when once that consciousness has disappeared. People have managed to mistake numerals for numbers, names for the things named, the mere devices of arithmetic for its proper subject-matter. Such experiences teach us how necessary it is to demand the highest exactness in manner of speech and writing. And I have taken pains to do justice to such demands, at any rate wherever it seemed to be of importance.

[1] The same idea and word were used by Dedekind (op. cit., p. 63); and the same idea but with the name 'equivalence' was used by Georg Cantor (cf. *Contributions to the Founding of the Theory of Transfinite Numbers*, Chicago and London, 1915, pp. 40, 86).

PRIMITIVE SIGNS

Introductory Remarks: Function, Concept, Relation

§ I

If we are asked to state what the word 'function' as used in mathematics originally stood for,* we easily fall into saying that a function of x is an expression formed, by means of the notations for sum, product, power, difference, and so on, out of 'x' and definite numbers. This attempt at a definition is not successful because a function is here said to be an *expression*, a combination of signs, and not what the combination designates. Accordingly another attempt would be made; we could try 'reference of an expression' instead of 'expression.' Now in the expression is an 'x,' which does not, like the sign '2,' stand for, but indefinitely indicates, a number. For different numerals put in the place of 'x,' we get, in general, a different reference. Suppose, e.g., that in the expression '$(2 + 3.x^2)x$,' instead of 'x' we put the number-signs '0,' '1', '2', '3', one after the other; we then get correspondingly as the reference of the expression the numbers 0, 5, 28, 87. Not one of the numbers so referred to can claim to be our function. The essence of the function comes out rather in the correspondence established between the numbers whose signs we put for 'x' and the numbers which then appear as the reference of our expression—a correspondence which is represented intuitively by the course of the curve whose equation is, in rectangular co-ordinates, '$y = (2 + 3.x^2)x$.' Accordingly, then, the essence of the *function* lies in the part of the expression which is there over and above the 'x.' The expression of a *function needs completion, is 'unsaturated.'* The letter 'x' only serves to keep places open for a numerical sign to be put in and complete the expression; and thus it enables us to recognize the special kind of need for completion that constitutes the peculiar nature of the function symbolized above. In what follows, the Greek letter 'ξ' will be used† instead of the letter 'x.' This

---

* Cf. my lecture *Function und Begriff*, Jena, 1891, and my essay *Ueber Begriff und Gegenstand* cited above. My *Begriffsschrift* of 1879 does not quite answer to my present view, and thus should only be used with caution to elucidate what I said here.

† Nothing, however, is fixed by this for our ideography. The 'ξ' never appears in the developments of the ideography itself, and I only use it in my exposition of it and in elucidations.

'keeping open' is to be understood in this way: All places in which 'ξ' stands must always be filled by the same sign and never by different ones. I call these places *argument-places*, and that whose sign or name takes these places in a given case I call the *argument* of the function for this case. The function is completed by the argument: I call what it becomes on completion the *value* of the function for the argument. We thus get a name of the value of a function for an argument when we fill the argument-places in the name of the function with the name of the argument. Thus, e.g., '$(2 + 3.1^2)1$' is a name of the number 5, composed of the function-name '$(2 + 3.\xi^2)\xi$' and '1.' The argument is not to be reckoned in with the function, but serves to complete the *function*, which is '*unsaturated*' by itself. When in the sequel an expression like 'the function $\Phi(\xi)$' is used, it is always to be observed that the only service rendered by 'ξ' in the symbol for the function is that it makes the argument-places recognizable; it does not imply that the essence of the function becomes changed when any other sign is substituted for 'ξ.'

§ 2

To the fundamental arithmetical operations mathematicians have added, as ways of forming functions, the process of proceeding to the limit as exemplified by infinite series, differential quotients and integrals; and finally the word 'function' has been understood in such a general way that the connexion between value of function and argument is in certain circumstances no longer expressed by signs of mathematical analysis, but can only be signified by words. Another extension has consisted in admitting complex numbers as arguments, and consequently also as values, of functions. In both directions I have gone still farther. While, indeed, hitherto the signs of analysis on the one hand have not always been sufficient, on the other hand not all of them have been employed to build up names of functions. For instance, '$\xi^2 = 4$' and '$\xi > 2$' were not allowed to count as names of functions; but I do allow them. But that indicates at the same time that the domain of values for functions cannot remain limited to numbers; for if I take as arguments of the function $\xi^2 = 4$ the numbers 0, 1, 2, 3, in succession, I do not get numbers. '$0^2 = 4$,' '$1^2 = 4$,' '$2^2 = 4$,' '$3^2 = 4$,' are expressions now of true, now of false thoughts. I express this by saying that the value of the function $\xi^2 = 4$ is the *truth-value* either of what is true or of what is false.* From this it can be seen that I do not intend to assert anything by merely writing down an equation, but that I only designate a truth-value; just as I do not intend to assert anything by simply writing down '2^2' but only *designate* a number. I say: 'The *names* '$2^2 = 4$' and '$3 > 2$' *stand for* the same truth-value' which I call for short *the True*. In the same manner '$3^2 = 4$' and '$1 > 2$' *stand for* the same truth-value, which I call for short *the False*, just as the name '2^2' *stands for* the number 4. Accordingly I say that the number 4 is the *reference* of '4' and of '2^2,' and that the True is the reference of '$3 > 2$.' But I distinguish the *sense* of a name from its *reference*. The names '2^2' and '$2 + 2$' have not the same *sense*, nor have '$2^2 = 4$' and '$2 + 2 = 4$.' The sense of the name for a truth-value I call a *thought*. I say further that what a name *expresses* is its sense, and what it *stands for* is its reference. I *designate* by a name that which it stands for.

The function $\xi^2 = 4$ can thus have only two values, the True for the arguments $+ 2$ and $- 2$ and the False for all other arguments.

Also the domain of what is admitted as argument must be extended—indeed, to objects quite generally. *Objects* stand opposed to functions. I therefore count as an *object* everything that is not a function: thus, examples of objects are numbers, truth-values, and the ranges to be introduced further on. The names of objects—or *proper names*—are not therefore accompanied by argument-places, but are 'saturated,' like the objects themselves.

§ 3

I use the words, 'the function $\Phi(\xi)$ has the same *range* as the function $\Psi(\xi)$,' to stand for the same thing as the words, 'the functions $\Phi(\xi)$ and $\Psi(\xi)$ have the same values for the same arguments.' This is the case with the functions $\xi^2 = 4$ and $3.\xi^2 = 12$, at least if numbers are taken as arguments. But we can further imagine the signs of evolution and multiplication defined in

---

* I have shown this more thoroughly in my essay *Ueber Sinn und Bedeutung* in the *Zeitschrift für Philos. und phil. Kritik*, Vol. 100, 1892, pp. 25–50.

such a manner that the function $(\xi^2 = 4) = (3.\xi^2 = 12)$ has the True as its value for any argument whatever. Here an expression of logic may also be used: 'The concept *square root of 4* has the same extension as the concept *something whose square when trebled makes 12*.' With those functions whose value is always a truth-value we can therefore say 'extension of the concept' instead of 'range of the function,' and it seems suitable to say that a *concept* is a function whose value is always a truth-value.

§ 4

Hitherto I have only dealt with functions of a single argument, but we can easily pass over to *functions with two arguments*. Such functions are *doubly in need of completion*; a function with one argument is obtained when a completion by means of one argument has been effected. Only by means of a repeated completion do we arrive at an object, and this object is then called the '*value*' of the function for the pair of arguments. Just as the letter 'ξ' served for functions of one argument, I use here the letters 'ξ' and 'ζ' in order to indicate the twofold unsaturatedness of a function of two arguments, as, e.g., in '$(\xi + \zeta)^2 + \zeta$.' By replacing 'ζ' by '1,' e.g., we [partly] saturate the function, in such a way that we have in $(\xi + 1)^2 + 1$ a function with only one argument. This way of using the letters 'ξ' and 'ζ' must always be kept in mind when an expression like 'the function $\Phi(\xi,\zeta)$' occurs.* I call the places in which 'ξ' stands 'ξ-argument-places,' and those in which 'ζ' stands 'ζ-argument-places.' I say that the ξ-argument-places are *related* (*verwandt*) to one another, and also the ζ-argument-places to one another, and I say that a ξ-argument-place is *not* related to a ζ-argument-place.

The functions with two arguments $\xi = \zeta$ and $\xi > \zeta$ always have a truth-value as their value—at least if the signs ' = ' and ' > ' are defined in a suitable way. I shall call such functions 'relations.' In the first relation, e.g., 1 stands to 1, and in general every object to itself; in the second, e.g., 2 stands to 1. We say that the object Γ 'stands in the relation $\Phi(\xi,\zeta)$ to' the object Δ, if $\Phi(\Gamma,\Delta)$ is the True. Similarly we say that the object Δ falls under the concept $\Phi(\xi)$ if $\Phi(\Delta)$ is the True. It is premised, of

* Cf. the second footnote to § 1.

course, that both the functions $\Phi(\xi)$ and $\Psi(\xi,\zeta)$ always have truth-values as their values.*

Functional Signs

§ 5

I have already said above that a mere equation is to make no assertion as yet; '$2 + 3 = 5$' just designates a truth-value, and it is not stated which of the two it is. Again, if I write '$(2 + 3 = 5) = (2 = 2)$' and took for granted that we know that $2 = 2$ is the True, yet I should not thereby have asserted that the sum of 2 and 3 is 5, but only designated the truth-value of: '$2 + 3 = 5$' stands for the same as '$2 = 2$.' Thus we need a special sign to assert that something or other is true. For this purpose I write the sign '$\vdash$' before the name of the truth-value, so that in '$\vdash 2^2 = 4$'† it is asserted that the square of 2 is 4. I make a distinction between *judgment* and *thought*, and understand by *judgment* the acknowledgment of the truth of a *thought*. I shall call the ideographic representation of a judgment by means of the sign '$\vdash$' an 'ideographic theorem' or more shortly a 'theorem.' I regard this sign '$\vdash$' as composed of a vertical line, which I call 'judgment-stroke,' and a horizontal line which I will simply call the horizontal.‡ This mostly occurs combined with other signs, as here with the stroke of judgment, and is thus guarded against confusion with the minus sign. Wherever it occurs by itself it must be made somewhat longer.

---

* Here there is a difficulty which may easily obscure the real state of affairs and thus arouse distrust of the correctness of my view. If we compare the expression 'the truth-value of: Δ falls under the concept $\Phi(\xi)$' with '$\Phi(\Delta)$,' we see that to the '$\Phi(\ )$' there properly corresponds 'the truth-value of: ( ) falls under the concept $\Phi(\xi)$' and not 'the concept $\Phi(\xi)$.' The last words do not therefore really designate a concept (in my sense of the word), though they have the appearance of doing so by their linguistic form. With regard to the awkward position in which language here finds itself, cf. my essay *Ueber Begriff und Gegenstand*.

† I often use here, in a preliminary way, the notations of sum, product, and power in order to make it easier to form examples, and to facilitate understanding by means of hints, although these signs are not yet defined in this place. But we must keep in view the fact that nothing is made to rest upon the reference these signs may have.

‡ In my *Begriffsschrift* I called this the content-stroke and at that time I expressed by the words 'possible content of judgment' what I have now learned to distinguish into truth-value and thought. Cf. my essay *Ueber Sinn und Bedeutung* cited above.

than the minus sign for purposes of distinction. I regard it as a name of a function, in this way: $-\varDelta$ is the True if $\varDelta$ is the True, and the False if $\varDelta$ is not the True.* $-\xi$ is a function whose value is always a truth-value; that is (*v. supra*) it is a concept. Under this concept there falls the True, and only the True. Thus ' $-2^2 = 4$' stands for the same thing as '$2^2 = 4$,' viz. the True. In order to do away with brackets, I lay down that all that stands to the right of the horizontal is to be taken as a whole and regarded as occupying the argument-place of the function $-\xi$, unless *brackets* forbid this. The sign ' $-2^2 = 5$' stands for the False, and thus for the same thing as '$2^2 = 5$,' whereas ' -2,' on the other hand, stands for the False, and thus for something different from the number 2. If $\varDelta$ is a truth-value, $-\varDelta$ is the same truth-value, and thus $\varDelta = (-\varDelta)$ is the True. But this is the False if $\varDelta$ is not a truth-value; so that we can say that

$$\varDelta = (-\varDelta)$$

is the truth-value of: $\varDelta$ is a truth-value.

Thus $-\Phi(\xi)$ is a concept and $-\Phi(\xi,\zeta)$ is a relation, whether or not $\Phi(\xi)$ is a concept and $\Phi(\xi,\zeta)$ is a relation.

Of the two signs out of which the sign '$\vdash$' is composed the judgment-stroke alone contains the act of assertion.

§ 6

We need no sign to declare that a truth-value is the False, if only we have a sign by which either truth-value is changed into the other. This sign is also indispensable on other grounds. I now lay down that the value of the function $\top\!\!\!-\xi$ is to be the False for every argument for which the value of the function $-\xi$ is the True. For all other arguments the value of our function is to be the True. Thus $\top\!\!\!-\xi$ is a function whose value is always a truth-value; it is a concept under which all objects fall with the single

---

* Of course the sign '$\varDelta$' must not be devoid of reference; it must stand for an object; names without reference may not occur in our ideography. The above arrangement is made so that ' $-\varDelta$' stands for something under all circumstances so long as '$\varDelta$' stands for something. If not, ' $-\xi$' would not stand for a concept with sharp boundaries—and thus would not stand for a concept in my sense at all. I here use *capital Greek letters* as if they were names standing for something although I do not specify a reference for them. In the actual developments of my ideography they will not occur any more than 'ξ' and 'ζ.'

exception of the True. From this it follows that '$\top\varDelta$' always stands for the same thing as '$\top(-\varDelta)$' and '$-\top\varDelta$' and '$-\top(-\varDelta)$' Thus we regard '$\top$' as compounded of the little vertical stroke (*stroke of negation*) and the two bits of the horizontal stroke; each of these may be regarded as a *horizontal* in our sense. The transition from '$\top(-\varDelta)$' or '$-\top\varDelta$' to '$\top\varDelta$' or from '$--\varDelta$' to '$-\varDelta$,' I call *amalgamation of horizontals*.

By our convention, $\top 2^2 = 5$ is the True; and thus: $\vdash 2^2 = 5$, in words: $2^2 = 5$ is not the True or, the square of 2 is not 5. So also: $\vdash 2$.

§ 7

I have already used the sign of equality in an incidental way to form examples, but it is necessary to lay down something more accurate about it. The sign '$\varGamma = \varDelta$' is to stand for the True if $\varGamma$ is the same as $\varDelta$, and the False in all other cases.

In order to dispense with brackets as far as possible, I lay down that all that stands on the left of the sign of equality as far as the nearest horizontal line is to denote the ξ-argument of the function $\xi = \zeta$, in so far as *brackets* do not forbid this; and that all that stands on the right of the sign of equality as far as the next sign of equality is to denote the ζ-argument of that function, in so far as *brackets* do not forbid this.[A]

A Cf. the use of brackets in § 5.

FREGE ON DEFINITIONS—I

Grundgesetze der Arithmetik, Vol. ii, Sections 56–67

Principles of Definition. 1. *Principle of Completeness*

§ 56

A DEFINITION of a concept (of a possible predicate) must be complete; it must unambiguously determine, as regards any object, whether or not it falls under the concept (whether or not the predicate is truly assertible of it). Thus there must not be any object as regards which the definition leaves in doubt whether it falls under the concept; though for us men, with our defective knowledge, the question may not always be decidable. We may express this metaphorically as follows: the concept must have a sharp boundary. If we represent concepts in extension by areas on a plane, this is admittedly a picture that may be used only with caution, but here it can do us good service. To a concept without sharp boundary there would correspond an area that had not a sharp boundary-line all round, but in places just vaguely faded away into the background. This would not really be an area at all; and likewise a concept that is not sharply defined is wrongly termed a concept. Such quasi-conceptual constructions cannot be recognized as concepts by logic; it is impossible to lay down precise laws for them. The law of excluded middle is really just another form of the requirement that the concept should have a sharp boundary. Any object Δ that you choose to take either falls under the concept Φ or does not fall under it; *tertium non datur*. E.g. would the sentence 'any square root of 9 is odd' have a comprehensible sense at all if *square root of 9* were not a concept with a sharp boundary? Has the question 'Are we still Christians?' really got a sense, if it is indeterminate whom the predicate 'Christian' can truly be asserted of, and who must be refused it?

§ 57

Now from this it follows that the mathematicians' favourite procedure, piecemeal definition, is inadmissible. The procedure is this: First they give the definition for a particular case—e.g. for positive integers—and make use of it; then, many theorems later, there follows a second definition for another case—e.g. for negative integers and zero—; here they often commit the further mistake of making specifications all over again for the case they have already dealt with. Even if in fact they avoid contradictions, in principle their method does not rule them out. What is more, as a rule they do not attain to completeness, but leave over some cases, as to which they make no specification; and many are naïve enough to employ the word or symbol for these cases too, as if they had given it something to stand for. Such piecemeal definition is a procedure comparable to drawing the boundary of a part of a surface in bits, perhaps without making them join up. But the chief mistake is that they are already using the symbol or word for theorems before it has been completely defined— often, indeed, with a view to further development of the definition itself. So long as it is not completely defined, or known in some other way, what a word or symbol stands for, it may not be used in an exact science—least of all with a view to further development of its own definition.

§ 58

Now, of course, it must be admitted that scientific progress, which has been effected by conquering wider and wider domains of numbers, made such a procedure almost inevitably necessary; and this necessity might serve as an excuse.* It would indeed have

---

* Thus, Peano says (*Revue de mathématique*, pt. VI, pp. 60–61): 'Frege requires one definition alone for every sign. And this is my opinion too, if it is a matter of a sign not containing variable letters (F_2, § 1, p. 7). But if the *definiendum* contains variable letters, i.e. is a function of such letters, then, so far as I can see, it is in general necessary to give conditional or hypothetical definitions of the expression (ibid., p. 7'), and to give as many definitions as there are kinds of entities on which we perform this operation. Thus the formula a + b will be first defined when a and b are integers, then a second time when they are fractions, then again when they are irrational or complex. The same sign + is met with between infinite and transfinite numbers (F_1 VI) and then a new definition must be given. It is met with again between two vectors, and will be defined over again; and so on. With the progress of science the meaning of this same formula is always being further extended. The various meanings of the symbol a + b have common properties; but these are insufficient to determine all the values that this expression can have.

'The same happens for the formula a = b. In some cases its meaning can be assumed as a primitive idea, in others it is defined; and precisely in arithmetic, given the equality of whole numbers, equality is defined between rationals, between irrationals, between

been possible to replace the old symbols and terms by new ones, and logic really demands this; but that is a hard decision to make. And this horror over the introduction of new symbols or words is the cause of many obscurities in mathematics. The old definitions likewise could have been rejected as invalid, and new ones used, in order to set up the science over again from the beginning; but such a clean cut was never made, because the old definitions were believed indispensable for the beginnings of the science. Didactic requirements may also have made themselves heard in this connexion. In this way people have got used to piecemeal definition; and what was originally an awkward makeshift became customary, and was admitted as one of the legitimate methods of science. The result is that nowadays hardly anybody is shocked when a symbol is first defined for a limited domain and then used in order to define the same symbol once more for a wider domain; for general custom has a power of justifying

imaginary numbers, etc. In geometry it is usual to define equality between two areas or two volumes, equality between two vectors, etc. With the progress of science, the need is more and more felt to extend the meaning of the expression a = b. The various meanings have common properties, but I do not see how they suffice to determine all the possible meanings of equality.

'Moreover, there is a wide diversity of opinion between various authors as regards the concept of equality. A study of this question would be very useful, especially if it were carried out with the aid of symbols as well as words.'

Peano here appeals to a practical need; but this does not upset the reasons I mentioned in my letter to him. It may be difficult to satisfy the demands of logic always in giving definitions; but it must be possible.

We may perhaps allow several conditional definitions of the same symbol when it is obvious from their form that they collectively cover all possible cases and do not make multiple specifications for any case, and when none of these partial definitions is used before they are all given—none, therefore, is used in another partial definition. In this case the definitions *formally* admit of being combined into a single definition. But this form of definition is best avoided, if possible.

In regard to the *equals* sign we shall do well to keep to our convention that equality is complete coincidence, identity. Of course bodies equal in volume are not identical, but they have the same volume. The signs on either side of the *equals* sign must thus in this case be taken as signs not for bodies but for their volumes, or for the numerical values obtained by measuring in terms of the same unit volume. We shall not speak of equal vectors, but rather of a certain attribute of the vectors (let us call it 'directed length') which can be the same in different vectors. On this view, the progress of science will not require us to widen the reference of the formula 'a = b'; we shall merely take into account new attributes (*modi*) of objects.

In his last sentence Peano coolly makes a monstrous assertion. If mathematicians have divergent opinions about equality, this means nothing less than that mathematicians disagree as to the content of their science; and if we regard science as essentially consisting of thoughts, not of words and symbols, it means that there is no united science of mathematics at all—that mathematicians just do not understand one another. For almost all arithmetical propositions, and many geometrical ones, depend for their sense, directly or indirectly, upon the sense of the word 'equals.'

what is done, just as fashion can give the cachet of beauty to the most detestable mode. It is all the more necessary to emphasize that logic cannot recognize as concepts quasi-conceptual constructions that are still fluid and have not yet been given definitive and sharp boundaries, and that therefore logic must reject all piecemeal definition. For if the first definition is already complete and has drawn sharp boundaries, then either the second definition draws the same boundaries—and then it must be rejected, because its content ought to be proved as a theorem—or it draws different ones—and then it contradicts the first one. For example, we may define a conic section as the intersection of a plane with a conical surface of rotation. When once we have done this, we may not define it over again, e.g. as a curve whose equation in Cartesian co-ordinates is of the second degree; for now that has to be proved. Likewise we cannot now define it as a plane figure whose equation in linear co-ordinates is of the second degree; for that would also include the point-pair, which cannot be regarded as the intersection of a plane and a conic surface. Here, then, the boundary of the concept is not drawn in the same way, and it would be a mistake to use here the same term 'conic section.' If the second definition is not ruled out by the first one in either of these ways, that is possible only because the first one is incomplete and has left the concept unfinished, i.e. in a condition in which it may not be employed at all—in particular, not for definitions.

§ 59

It will be not unprofitable to give an example, so as to counterbalance the abstractness of these remarks. E. Heine sets up the following definition:*

'Number-signs are called equal or interchangeable when they belong to equal series of numbers, and unequal or non-interchangeable when they belong to unequal series (§ 1, Def. 3).'

What would people say to the following definition?

'Signs are called white when they belong to white objects.' Now I may legitimately take, as a sign for the white sheet of

---

* *Die Elemente der Funktionenlehre*, § 2, Def. 2 (Crelle, Vol. 74). From my here raising only one objection to this definition it must not be inferred that I regard it as otherwise unexceptionable.

paper that I have before me, a circular black patch, so long as I have not already employed this sign in some other way. And such a patch would now be white by definition. As against this, we must say: In using the expression 'if they belong to white objects,' the definition presupposes that we know what the word 'white' stands for; for otherwise it would be wholly unspecified what signs belong to white objects. Very well! If the word 'white' is known, we cannot want to define it over again. We ought to regard it as quite self-evident that a word may not be defined by means of itself; for if we do that we are in one breath treating the word as known and as unknown. If it is known, a definition is at least superfluous; if it is not known, it cannot serve for the purpose of definition. This is so obvious, and yet people sin against it so often! We get the same case for Heine's definition. The use of the words 'if they belong to equal series of numbers' presupposes that we know what the word 'equal' stands for, and this is the very word that is to be defined.

§ 60

Heine would probably remark in answer to this that he is not presupposing that we know what the word 'equal' stands for in all cases; in his Def. 3, § 1, its reference is supposed already given only for unbracketed number-series, whereas here he is speaking of bracketed number-series and other symbols. Besides the reasons against this procedure given above, it may be added that double definition of a word is objectionable because then we are left in doubt whether the definitions do not contradict each other. People ought at least to ask for a proof that there is no contradiction; but this duty is regularly evaded, and indeed in Heine there is not to be found a trace of such a proof. In general, we must reject a way of defining that makes the correctness of a definition depend on our having first to carry out a proof; for this makes it extraordinarily difficult to check the rigour of the deduction, since it is necessary to inquire, as regards each definition, whether any propositions have to be proved before laying it down—an inquiry, however, that is almost always left undone.

People are hardly ever conscious of this sort of gap, which is therefore specially dangerous as regards rigour. In arithmetic it just will not do to make any assertion you like without proof or with a sham proof, and then wait and see if anybody succeeds in proving its falsity; on the contrary, it must be demanded that every assertion that is not completely self-evident should have a real proof; and this involves that any expressions or symbols used in the proof, unless they may be regarded as generally known, must be introduced in an unexceptionable way.

And moreover it is so easy to avoid a plurality of definitions for one and the same symbol. Instead of first defining a symbol for a limited domain and then using it for the purpose of defining itself in regard to a wider domain, we need only choose different signs, confining the reference, of the first, once for all, to the narrower domain; in this way the first definition is now complete and draws sharp boundary-lines. This in no way prejudges the relation between the reference of one sign and that of the other; we can investigate this, without its being possible that the result of the investigation should make it questionable whether the definitions were justified.

It really is worth the trouble to invent a new symbol if we can thus remove not a few logical difficulties and ensure the rigour of the proofs. But many mathematicians seem to have so little feeling for logical purity and accuracy that they will use a word to stand for three or four different things, sooner than make the frightful decision to invent a new word.

§ 61

Piecemeal definition likewise makes the status of theorems uncertain. If, e.g., the words 'square root of 9' have been defined with a restriction to the domain of positive integers, then we can prove, e.g., the proposition that there is only one square root of 9; but this is at once overthrown when we extend our treatment to negative numbers and supplement the definition accordingly. But who can tell if we have now reached a definitive proposition? Who can tell but that we may see ourselves driven to recognize four square roots of 9? How are we really going to tell that there are no more than two square roots of -1? So long as we have no final and complete definitions, it is impossible.   It may perhaps be objected that in that case some propositions would no longer hold good.   The same reason would go against admitting a second square root of 9.   In this way we never have really firm ground underfoot.   If we have no final definitions we likewise have no final theorems.   We never emerge from incompleteness and vagueness.

§ 62

We get the same case for a relation as for a concept: logic can recognize a relation only if it is determinate, as regards any one object and any other object, whether or not the one stands to the other in that relation.   Here too we have a *tertium non datur*; the case of its being undecided is ruled out.   If there were a relation for which this requirement were not fulfilled, then the concepts that we can derive from it by partly filling it up (vol. i, § 30ᴮ) likewise would not have completely sharp boundaries, and would thus, strictly speaking, not be concepts at all, but inadmissible sham concepts.   If, e.g., the relation *greater than* is not completely defined, then it is likewise uncertain whether a quasi-conceptual construction obtained by partly filling it up, e.g. *greater than zero* or *positive*, is a proper concept.   For it to be a proper concept, it would have to be determinate whether, e.g., the Moon is greater than zero.   We may indeed specify that only numbers can stand in our relation, and infer from this that the Moon, not being a number, is also not greater than zero.   But with that there would have to go a complete definition of the word 'number,' and that is just what is most lacking.

It is just as regards the relation *greater than* that piecemeal, and therefore incomplete, definition, is, so to say, good form in mathematics.   The words 'greater than' are first defined in the domain of positive integers, i.e. incompletely.   The pseudo-relation thus obtained, which it is wrong to use at all, is then used in order to complete the first definition; and here, of course, one cannot always tell when the definition of the relation *greater than* is to count as complete.   For the relation of equality the case is

ᴮ This reference should rather be: '(Vol. i, §§ 4, 30).'

quite similar; here too piecemeal definition is absolutely a part of good form.* Nevertheless we must stick to our point: without complete and final definitions, we have no firm ground underfoot, we are not sure about the validity of our theorems, and we cannot confidently apply the laws of logic, which certainly presuppose that concepts, and relations too, have sharp boundaries.

§ 63

At this point it is easy to draw a conclusion in regard to functions that are neither concepts nor relations. Let us take as an example the expression 'the half of something,' which purports to be a name of such a function. Here the word 'something' is keeping a place open for the argument; it corresponds to the letter 'ξ' in '$\frac{1}{2}\xi$.' Such an expression can become part of a concept-name, e.g. 'something the half of which is less than one.'

Now if this last expression is actually to stand for a concept with sharp boundaries, then it must be determinate, e.g., as regards the Moon whether the half of it is less than one. But in order that this should happen, the expression 'the half of the Moon' must have a reference; i.e. there must be one and only one object designated by this. Now according to common usage this is not the case, for nobody knows which half of the Moon is meant. So here, too, we must make a more precise specification, so that it is determined, as regards every object, which object is the half of it; otherwise it is wrong to use the expression 'the half of x' with the definite article. Thus a first-level function of one argument must always be such as to yield an object as its value, whatever object we may take as its argument—whatever object we may use to 'saturate' the function.†

---

* In practice, indeed, when mathematicians give proofs, they do all treat equality as identity; although in theory most of them will not allow that this is true. But nobody is going to say, e.g., that the equation '$4x - 3 = 3$' has the roots 6/4 and 3/2, on the ground that 6/4 is indeed equal to 3/2 but does not coincide with it. If 6/4 and 3/2 do not coincide, then they are different, and our equation has at least two different roots. It is remarkable to see what a frightful conflict there is, for many mathematicians, between their explicit theory and their tacitly adopted practice. But if equality in mathematics is identity, then a plurality of definitions for it is a senseless procedure.

† Cf. the remarks about the function in Vol. i. Cf. also the author's essay *Function und Begriff* (Pohle, Jena, 1891).

§ 64

We must make the corresponding requirement as regards functions with two arguments. The expression

'the sum of one object and another object'

purports to be the name of such a function. Here too, then, it must be determinate, as regards any one object and any other object, which object is the sum of the one and the other; and there must always be such an object. If that is not the case, then it is likewise indeterminate which object gives the result one when added to itself. In that case, therefore, the words 'something that gives the result one when added to itself' do not stand for any concept with sharp boundaries, i.e. for anything that can be used in logic. And the question how many objects there are that give the result one when added to themselves is unanswerable.

But can we not stipulate that the expression 'the sum of one object and another object' is to have a reference only when both objects are numbers? In that case, you may well think, the concept *something that gives the result one when added to itself* is one with sharp boundaries; for now we know that no object that is not a number falls under it. E.g. the Moon does not fall under it, since the sum of the Moon and the Moon is not one. This is wrong. On the present view, the sentence 'the sum of the Moon and the Moon is one' is neither true nor false; for in either case the words 'the sum of the Moon and the Moon' would have to stand for something, and this was expressly denied by the suggested stipulation. Our sentence would be comparable, say, to the sentence 'Scylla had six dragon necks.' This sentence likewise is neither true nor false, but fiction, for the proper name 'Scylla' designates nothing. Such sentences can indeed be objects of a scientific treatment, e.g. of myth; but no scientific investigation can issue in them. If our sentence 'the sum of the Moon and the Moon is not one' were a scientific one, then it would assert that the words 'the sum of the Moon and the Moon' and the word 'one' did not coincide in reference; but with the stipulation suggested above, the former words would not have any reference; accordingly we could not truly assert either that their reference did coincide with the reference of the word 'one' or that it did not coincide with it. Thus it would be impossible to answer the question whether the sum of the Moon and the Moon is one, or whether the Moon falls under the concept *something that gives the result one when added to itself*. In other words, what we have just called a concept would not be a genuine concept at all, since it would lack sharp boundaries. But when once we have introduced the expression '*a* added to *b* gives the result *c*,' we can no longer stop the construction of a concept-name like 'something that gives the result one when added to itself.' If people would actually try to lay down laws that stopped the formation of such concept-names as this, which, though linguistically possible, are inadmissible, they would soon find the task exceedingly difficult and probably impracticable. The only way left open is to give to the words 'sum,' 'addition,' etc., if one means to use them at all, such definitions that the concept-names constructed out of the words in a linguistically correct manner stand for concepts with sharp boundaries and are thus admissible.

Thus the requirement we have here set up—that every first-level function of two arguments must have an object as its value for any one object as its first argument and any other object as its second—is a consequence of the requirement that concepts must have sharp boundaries and that we may not tolerate expressions which seem by their structure to stand for a concept but only create an illusion of one, just as we may not admit proper names that do not actually designate an object.

§ 65

What has been said about verbal expressions holds good also for arithmetical symbols. If the sign of addition has been completely defined, then

$$'\xi + \xi = \zeta'$$

gives us the name of a relation—the relation of single to double. If that is not the case, then we cannot say whether the equation

$$'x + x = 1'$$

has an unique solution or several solutions. Now anybody will answer: 'I forbid anything but numbers to be taken into account at all.' We dealt above with a similar objection; here we may throw light on the matter from other sides. If anybody wants to exclude from consideration all objects that are not numbers, he must first say what he takes 'number' to mean, and then further extension of the term is inadmissible. Such a restriction would have to be incorporated in the definition, which would thus take some such form as: 'If a and b are numbers, then $a + b$ stands for . . .' We should have a conditional definition.* But the sign of addition has not been defined unless every possible complex symbol of the form '$a + b$' has a definite reference, whatever proper names with a reference may take the places of 'a' and 'b.' If on the contrary such complex symbols are defined, e.g. only for the case when symbols for real integers are taken instead of 'a' and 'b,' then what has really been defined is only the complex symbols, not the sign of addition: an offence against the second principle of definition, which we still have to discuss. And yet people cannot help imagining they know what the sign of addition stands for; and accordingly they employ it also in cases for which no definition has been given.

As soon as people aim at generality in propositions they will need in arithmetical formulae not only symbols for definite objects—e.g. the proper name '2'—but also letters that only indicate and do not designate;† and this already leads them, quite unawares, beyond the domain within which they have defined their symbols. One may try to avoid the dangers thus arising by not making the letters indicate objects in general (as I did), but only those of a domain with fixed boundaries. Let us suppose for once that the concept *number* has been sharply defined; let it be laid down that italic letters are to indicate only numbers; and let the sign of addition be defined only for numbers. Then in the proposition '$a + b = b + a$' we must mentally add the conditions that a and b are numbers; and these conditions, not being expressed, are easily forgotten.‡ But let us deliberately not forget them for once! By a well-known law of logic, the proposition

'if a is a number and b is a number then $a + b = b + a$'

* Cf. the author's letter to Sig. Peano, *Revue de Mathématiques*, Vol. i, pp. 53 ff.
† Cf. Vol. i, pp. 31–32.
‡ E.g. do people always bear it in mind, when they extend the number-domain, that thereby the sense of the conditions is changed; that all general propositions proved up to that point acquire a new content of thought; and likewise that all the proofs break down?

can be transformed into the proposition

'if $a + b$ is not equal to $b + a$, and a is a number, then b is not a number'

and here it is impossible to maintain the restriction to the domain of numbers. The force of the situation works irresistibly towards the breaking down of such restrictions. But in this case our antecedent clause

'if $a + b$ is not equal to $b + a$'

is senseless, assuming that the sign of addition has not been completely defined.

Here again we likewise see that the laws of logic presuppose concepts with sharp boundaries, and therefore also complete definitions for names of functions, like the *plus* sign.* In vol. i we expressed this as follows: every function-name must have a reference. Accordingly all conditional definitions, and any procedure of piecemeal definition, must be rejected. Every symbol must be completely defined at a stroke, so that, as we say, it acquires a reference.

All of this hangs very close together, and may be regarded as derived from the principle of completeness in definitions.

2 *Principle of Simplicity in the Expression defined.*†

§ 66

Given the reference of an expression and of a part of it, obviously the reference of the remaining part is not always determined. So we may not define a symbol or word by defining an expression in which it occurs, whose remaining parts are known. For it would first be necessary to investigate whether— to use a readily understandable metaphor from algebra—the equation can be solved for the unknown, and whether the unknown is unambiguously determined. But as I have already said above, it is not feasible to make the correctness of a definition depend on the outcome of such an investigation—one which, moreover, would perhaps be quite impracticable. Rather, the definition must have the character of an equation that is solved

---

* It is self-evident that certain functions are indefinable, because of their logical simplicity. But these too must have values for all arguments.

† Vol. i, § 33, 3.

for the unknown, and on the other side of which nothing unknown occurs any longer.

Still less will it do to define two things with one definition;
any definition must, on the contrary, contain a single sign, and
fix the reference of this sign. One equation alone cannot be used
to determine two unknowns.

Moreover, we sometimes find a whole system of definitions
set up, each one containing several words that need definition,
in such a way that each of these words occurs in several of the
definitions. This is like a system of equations with several unknowns; and here again it remains completely doubtful whether
the equations can be solved and whether the solution is unambiguously determined.

Any symbol or word can indeed be regarded as consisting of
parts; but we do not deny its simplicity unless, given the general
rules of grammar, or of the symbolism, the reference of the whole
would follow from the reference of the parts, and these parts occur
also in other combinations and are treated as independent signs
with a reference of their own. In this sense, then, we may say:
the word (symbol) that is defined must be simple. Otherwise it
might come about that the parts were also defined separately
and that these definitions contradicted the definition of the whole.

Of course names of functions, because of their characteristic
unsaturatedness,' cannot stand alone on one side of a defining
equation; their argument-places must always be filled up somehow or other. In my ideography, as we have seen,* this is done
by means of italic letters, which must then occur on the other
side as well. In language, instead of these, there occur pronouns
and particles ('something,' 'what,' 'it') which indicate indefinitely.
This is no violation of our principle; for these letters, pronouns,
particles do not stand for anything, but only indicate.

§ 67

Often there is an offence against both principles of definition
at once. E.g. the *equals* sign is defined along with what stands to
the right and left of it. In this case the *equals* sign has already been
defined previously, but only in an incomplete way. Thus there

* Vol. i, § 33, 5.

arises a queer twilight; the *equals* sign is treated in a half-and-half way, as known and again as unknown. On the one hand, it looks as though we were meant to recall the earlier definition and extract from it something to go towards determining what now appears on the right and left sides of the *equals* sign. On the other hand, however, this earlier definition will not do for our present case. A similar thing happens over other signs too. This twilight is needed by many mathematicians for the performance of their logical conjuring tricks. The ends that are meant to be achieved in this way are unexceptionably attained through our transformation of an equality that holds generally into an equality between ranges of values, by Axiom V (vol. i, § 3, § 9, § 20).

It has not been my aim to give here a complete survey of all that has to be observed in giving definitions; I will content myself with stating these two principles, the ones against which mathematicians sin oftenest.

FREGE ON DEFINITIONS—II

Grundgesetze der Arithmetik, Vol. ii, Sections 139-44, 146-7

*Construction of new Objects; Views of R. Dedekind,
H. Hankel, R. Stolz.*

§ 139

DEDEKIND gives the name *section* to a division of the rational number system into two classes such that any number in the first class is smaller than any number in the second; and he shows that every rational number generates a section, or properly speaking two sections, but that there are sections not generated by any rational number. He then goes on to say (§ 4, p. 14):[A]

'Now whenever we are presented with a section (A_1, A_2) not generated by any rational number, we construct a new, irrational number a, which we regard as completely defined by this section; we shall say that the number a corresponds to this section, or generates this section.'

It is in this construction that the heart of the matter lies. We must first notice that this procedure is quite different from what is done in formalist arithmetic—the introduction of a new sort of figures and special rules for manipulating them. There the difficulty is how to tell whether these new rules may turn out to conflict with those laid down previously and how to straighten out such a conflict. Here we are concerned with the question whether construction is possible at all; whether, if it is possible, it is unrestrictedly possible; or whether certain laws must be observed when we are constructing. In the last case it would first have to be proved that the construction was justified in accordance with these laws, before we might perform the act of creation. These inquiries are here completely lacking, and thus there is lacking the main thing—what the proofs carried out by means of irrational numbers depend upon for their cogency.

[A] The reference is to his *Stetigkeit und irrationale Zahlen*, Vieweg & Sohn, Braunschweig, 1892.

173

The power of construction, if it does exist, cannot in any case be unrestricted; as we see from the fact that no object combining inconsistent properties can be constructed.

§ 140

We are led to the same result by the following consideration. In mathematics it is no rare thing for an auxiliary object to be needed in order to prove a proposition; i.e. an object not mentioned in the proposition itself. In geometry we have auxiliary lines and points. In arithmetic, similarly, we have auxiliary numbers. E.g. a square root of -1 is needed in order to prove propositions that deal only with real numbers. In number theory we prove by means of the indices that the congruences '$x^n \equiv 1$' and '$x^\delta \equiv 1$' on the prime modulus p have the same roots, δ being the greatest common factor of n and $p - 1$; here we require a primitive root, viz. the base of the indices, as an auxiliary number. In our proofs too auxiliary objects have already occurred: cf. vol. i, § 94. We likewise saw there how to get rid of such an object again. For there must be no mention of it in the proposition to be proved, although we need some of its properties in the proof (e.g. we need the property of being a primitive root in relation to the prime number p, in proving the proposition of number theory mentioned above). We must first introduce conditional clauses, expressing the supposition that an object has the said properties. If we know such an object, we can eliminate the conditions. If we cannot mention such an object (as happens in our example, where we are speaking not of this or that definite prime number, but of a prime number in general) then at any rate we must prove that there always is such an object (e.g. a primitive root in relation to the prime number p). How much easier this would be if we could without more ado construct the objects required! If we do not know whether there is a number whose square is -1, then we construct one. If we do not know whether there is a primitive root in relation to a prime number, then we construct one. If we do not know whether there is a straight line passing through certain points, then we construct one. Unfortunately this is too easy to be right. Certain limits on the power of construction would have to be admitted.

If an arithmetician admits in general the possibility of construction, his most important task will be a clear exposition of the laws that must be observed, in order that then he may go on to prove, before every single act of creation, that it is permitted according to these laws. Otherwise everything becomes vague, and proofs degenerate into a mere sham, a comfortable make-believe.

§ 141

Hankel says (*Theorie der complexen Zahlensysteme*, § 7 *ad init.*):

'In this section we are dealing with numbers α, β, . . . , linearly compounded out of the units ι_1, ι_2, ι_3, . . . ι_n, which obey the rules of multiplication expressed in the relations:

$$\iota_1\iota_1 = 0,\ \iota_2\iota_2 = 0,\ \ldots\ \iota_n\iota_n = 0, \iota_k\iota_m = -\ \iota_m\iota_k.'$$

With these so-called units he then proves, e.g., the multiplication theorem for determinants; or rather, he imagines that he proves it. Really there is just a stupendous conjuring trick; for nowhere is it proved that there are such units, nowhere is it proved that we have the right to construct them. It is not even proved that the properties ascribed to these units are not mutually contradictory. In fact it remains obscure what these properties actually are; for nowhere is it stated what a product must be taken to be in this case. Properly, the propositions given above, '$\iota_1\iota_1 = 0$' and the rest, must be introduced as conditions; and the law of multiplication for determinants must also appear as depending on these conditions. Eliminating the conditions remains an unsolved problem if we use this method of proof. A solution would be possible if 'ι_1,' 'ι_2,' and so on were proper names of objects satisfying the conditions. We do not know what a product or a sum is for this sort of numbers. But let us just suppose we did know; in that case we should know of ι_1 the property that $\iota_1\iota_1 = 0$—a property shared with ι_2, ι_3, etc.—and further we should know certain relations in which ι_1 would have to stand to other unknowns, ι_2, ι_3, etc. Clearly ι_1 is not determined by this. We do not know how many such objects there are, nor whether there are any at all. Even the class these objects are supposed to belong to is undetermined. Let us suppose that such a class contains the objects

$$\iota_1,\ \iota_2,\ \ldots\ \iota_9.$$

Then the class containing only the objects

$$\iota_1 \; \iota_2 \; \iota_3, \; \iota_4 \; \iota_5 \; \iota_6, \; \iota_7 \; \iota_8 \; \iota_9,$$

has the same general property; so likewise has the class containing only the objects

$$\iota_1 \iota_4 \iota_7, \; \iota_2 \iota_5 \iota_8, \; \iota_3 \iota_6 \iota_9;$$

so have many other classes. Consequently, even the class these objects belong to is not determined; still less are they themselves determined; and it is impossible to regard 'ι_1,' 'ι_2,' etc., as proper names that have reference, like '2' and '3.' The only thing left is to regard them as indicating objects, like 'a,' 'b,' 'c,' not as standing for, or designating, objects. But then the question is whether there are objects satisfying the conditions mentioned above. These conditions are not even complete; for there is missing the condition that the product of an ordinary number and a product of certain ι-numbers is different from the product of another ordinary number and the same product of ι-numbers. Otherwise, given

$$a.\iota_1\iota_2\iota_3 = b.\iota_1\iota_2\iota_3,$$

we could not infer $a = b$.

Now the proof that there are such ι-objects is lacking. Perhaps Hankel believed he was constructing them by the words quoted above; but he still owes us the proof that he was entitled so to construct them.

§ 142

If we had tried to carry out in our ideography Hankel's proof of his proposition about determinants, we should, so to say, have run our noses against this obstacle. The reason why it is so easily overlooked with Hankel's method of proof is that the assumptions are not all written down in Euclid's style and strict precautions taken to use no others. If this were done, assumptions could not so easily be made to vanish by a conjuring trick.

What is more, many proofs carried out by means of the imaginary unit stand on no firmer footing than Hankel's proof, which we have just been talking about. The reason why the mistake hits you in the eye more in the latter case is not that there is any essential logical difference, but that people are already used to the imaginary unit more than they are to alternating numbers. One need only use a word or symbol often enough, and the impression will be produced that this proper name stands for something; and this impression will grow so strong in course of time that in the end hardly anybody has any doubt about the matter.

§ 143

Creative definitions are a first-rate discovery. Otto Stolz writes thus:*

'6. *Definition.* In the case where lim $(f:g)$ is a positive number or is $+\infty$, there shall be a thing distinct from the moments, denoted by $u(f):u(g)$, and satisfying the equation $u(g).[u(f):u(g)] = u(f)$.'

Let us compare this with the following:

'*Definition.* If the points A, B, C, D, E, F are so situated that the lines joining AD, BE, CF pass through the same point, then there shall be a thing that is a straight line and passes through the intersections of the straight lines joining AB and DE, BC and EF, CA and FD.'

The cases will be pronounced entirely different; but no essential logical difference will come out on more precise investigation. We do not use the second definition; instead, we enunciate and prove a theorem. But the inestimable advantage of a creative definition is that it saves us a proof. And it is child's play to attain this advantage; we need only choose as a title the word 'definition' instead of the word 'theorem.' This is certainly an urgent necessity, otherwise the nature of the proposition might be mistaken.

We find another example of a creative definition on p. 34 (op. cit.), where we read:

'1. *Definition.* "If in case (D_1) no magnitude of System (I) satisfies the equation $box = a$, then it shall be satisfied by *one and only one new thing not found in* (I); this may be symbolized by aub, since this symbol has not yet been used. We thus have

$$bo(aub) = (aub)oa = a."\dagger$$

---

* *Vorlesungen über allgemeine Arithmetik.* Part I, p. 211. Teubner, Leipzig, 1885.

† As regards o he says (p. 26): 'The combination o is called *thesis*.' We might conclude from the definite article that the symbol o had a definite reference. This, however, is not the case; it is meant just to indicate a combination. But what we are to understand by 'combination' and 'result of a combination' we are not told.

Since the new objects possess no further properties, we can assign them properties arbitrarily, so long as these are not mutually inconsistent.'

Creation is thus performed in several stages. After the first, the thing is indeed there, but it is, so to say, stark naked, devoid of the most necessary properties; these are assigned to it only in later creative acts, and it will then have to be hailed as the lucky owner of these properties. Admittedly the power of creating is here restricted by the proviso that the properties must not be mutually inconsistent; an obvious restriction, but one very hard to observe. How do we tell that properties are not mutually inconsistent? There seems to be no criterion for this except the occurrence of the properties in question in one and the same object. But the creative power with which many mathematicians credit them-selves thus becomes practically worthless. For as it is they must certainly prove, before they perform a creative act, that there is no inconsistency between the properties they want to assign to the object that is to be, or has already been, constructed; and apparently they can do this only by proving that there is an object with all these properties together. But if they can do that, they need not first construct such an object.

§ 144

Or is there perhaps still another way of proving consistency? If there were one, it would be of the highest significance for all mathematicians who credit themselves with a power of creating. And yet hardly anybody seems to concern himself with devising such a type of proof. Why not? Probably people think a proof of consistency superfluous, because any inconsistency would be noticed at once. What a fine thing if it were so! How simple all proofs would then be in their form! The proof of Pythagoras's theorem would go something like this:

'Suppose that the square on the hypotenuse were not equal in area to the squares on the other two sides taken together. Then there would be a contradiction between this supposition and the known axioms of geometry. Consequently our supposition is false, and the square on the hypotenuse is exactly equal in area to the squares on the other two sides taken together.'

It would be equally easy to prove the law of reciprocity for quadratic residues:

'Let p and q be primes, of which at least one is congruent to 1 modulo 4, and let p be a quadratic residue of q. Now suppose q were not a quadratic residue of p; this would obviously contradict our hypotheses and the known laws of arithmetic (anyone who does not see this does not count). Consequently our supposition is false, and q must be a quadratic residue of p.'

On these patterns it would be easy to carry out any proof. Unfortunately this method is too simple to be acceptable. We see well enough that not every contradiction lies quite open to view. Moreover, we have no reliable criterion for the cases when it is supposed possible to infer the absence of a contradiction from its not being apparent. In these circumstances the mathematicians' alleged power of creation must surely be considered worthless; for just where the exercise of it would be of value, it is tied up with conditions that apparently cannot be fulfilled. Besides, how do we know that avoidance of contradiction is the only thing to be observed in the act of construction?

§ 146

It has thus been made probable that a mathematician is denied the power of actual construction, or at any rate that it is tied up with conditions that render it worthless. As against this, somebody might indicate that we ourselves have nevertheless constructed new objects, viz. value-ranges (vol. i, §§ 3, 9, 10). What, then, did we do there? or rather, in the first place, what did we not do? We did not enumerate properties and then say: we construct a thing that is to have these properties. Rather, we said: If a (first-level) function (of one argument) and another function are such as always to have the same value for the same argument, then we may say instead that the range of values of the first is the same as that of the second. We are then recognizing something common to the two functions, and we call this the value-range of the first function and also the value-range of the second function. We must regard it as a fundamental law of logic that we are justified in thus recognizing something common to both, and that accordingly we may transform an equality holding generally into an equation (identity). This transformation must not be regarded as a definition; neither the word 'same' or the *equals* sign, nor the word 'value-range' or a complex symbol like '$\dot{\epsilon}\Phi(\epsilon)$,' nor both together, are defined by means of it. For the sentence

'the value-range of the first function is the same as the value-range of the second function'

is complex, and contains as a part the word 'same,' which must be regarded as completely known. Similarly the symbol '$\dot{\epsilon}\Phi(\epsilon) = \dot{a}\Psi(a)$' is complex and contains as a part the *equals* sign which is already known. So if we tried to regard our stipulation in § 3 as a definition, this would certainly be an offence against our second principle of definition.*

§ 147

People have indeed clearly already made use of the possibility of transformation that I have mentioned; only they have asserted coincidence of functions themselves rather than of value-ranges. When one function has in general the same value as another function for the same argument, it is usual to say: 'the first function is the same as the second' or 'the two functions coincide.' The expression is different from ours, but all the same here too we have an equality holding generally transformed into an equation (identity).†

Logicians have long since spoken of the extension of a concept, and mathematicians have used the terms set, class, manifold;

---

* In general, we must not regard the stipulations in Vol. i, with regard to the primitive signs, as definitions. Only what is logically complex can be defined; what is simple can only be pointed to.

† Likewise, very few mathematicians will take thought over using '$f = g$' to express the circumstance that $f(\xi)$ always has the same value as the function $g(\xi)$ for the same argument. This certainly involves a mistake, arising from a defective conception of the nature of a function. An isolated function-letter without a place for an argument is a monstrosity, just as an isolated functional symbol like '*sin*' is. For what is distinctive of a function, as compared with an object, is precisely its 'unsaturatedness,' its needing to be completed by an argument; and this feature must also come out in the symbolism. Such a symbolism as '$f = g$' is inadmissible, as is brought out by the fact that in particular cases it breaks down. If you put, e.g., $\xi^2 - 1$ for $f(\xi)$ and $(\xi - 1)(\xi + 1)$ for $g(\xi)$, then it hits you in the eye that you cannot write down anything corresponding to the equation '$f = g$.' But if symbolism is in order it must always be possible to make such a transition within the symbolism from general to particular. Accordingly the symbolism '$f = g$' cannot be recognized as correct; but nevertheless it shows that mathematicians have already made use of the possibility of our transformation.

what lies behind this is a similar transformation; for we may well suppose that what mathematicians call a set (etc.) is nothing other than an extension of a concept, even if they have not always been clearly aware of this.

What we are doing by means of our transformation is thus not really anything novel; but we do it with full awareness, appealing to a fundamental law of logic. And what we thus do is quite different from the lawless, arbitrary construction of numbers by many mathematicians.

If there are logical objects at all—and the objects of arithmetic are such objects—then there must also be a means of apprehending, of recognizing, them. This service is performed for us by the fundamental law of logic that permits the transformation of an equality holding generally into an equation. Without such a means a scientific foundation for arithmetic would be impossible. For us this serves towards the ends that other mathematicians intend to attain by constructing new numbers. We thus hope to be able to develop the whole wealth of objects and functions treated of in mathematics out of the germ of the eight functions whose names are enumerated in vol. i, § 31. Can our procedure be termed construction? Discussion of this question may easily degenerate to a quarrel over words. In any case our construction (if you like to call it that) is not unrestricted and arbitrary; the mode of performing it, and its legitimacy, are established once for all. And thus here the difficulties and objections vanish that in other cases make it questionable whether the construction is a logical possibility; and we may hope that by means of our value-ranges we shall attain what has been missed by following any other way.

FREGE AGAINST THE FORMALISTS
Grundgesetze der Arithmetik, Vol. ii, Sections 86–137

E. Heine's and J. Thomae's Theories of Irrational Numbers

§ 86

AT first sight the theories of E. Heine* and J. Thomae† seem almost to coincide with that of Cantor. There are numerical series and numerical sequences resembling Cantor's fundamental series; again, the allocation of signs to these series is regarded as specially important. Altogether, the mode of procedure is superficially very similar to Cantor's. Yet the similarity is less than might at first be supposed, and a separate and detailed examination of these theories is needed. These two theories basically agree, though Heine elaborates the main thesis more strictly than Thomae. And both deviate considerably from Cantor. Cantor in fact does not seem to regard numerical signs as empty, though his statements leave room for doubt and he may not have considered the point explicitly. Yet the essential thing for him is what the signs express (which, to be sure, he wishes to control by those signs) and not the signs themselves.

Now the peculiarity of Heine's theory is that it holds signs to be everything, and this is asserted even more explicitly by Thomae. Both writers also agree in finally abandoning this view, when they do eventually let their signs designate something, viz. the numerical series or numerical sequences corresponding to Cantor's fundamental series. But whereas we may take Cantor's fundamental series to consist of *abstract conceptual things* (to use his language) we have to think of these numerical series and numerical sequences of Heine and Thomae as composed of written or printed, visible, material figures. Thus the series are likely to be groups of such figures, which, in virtue of their spatial arrangement, present themselves to the eye as series. So we have here the peculiar situation that certain signs designate series or sequences, whose members in turn designate such series—and so on *ad infinitum*.

---

* Crelles Journal, Vol. 74, p. 172.

† *Elementare Theorie der analytischen Functionen einer complexen Veränderlichen*, 2nd edition Halle a.S. 1898, Sections 1 to 11.

§ 87

I shall quote the relevant statements of Heine and Thomae and then inquire into the reason for setting up these theories.

Heine writes:

> Suppose I am not satisfied to have nothing but positive rational numbers. I do not answer the question, What is a number? by defining number conceptually, say by introducing irrationals as limits whose *existence* is presupposed. I define from the standpoint of the pure formalist and *call certain tangible signs numbers*. Thus the existence of these numbers is not in question.

Here Heine mentions existence twice, and with good reason; for we have seen how inadequately this very question of existence was answered by Cantor. This is why Heine calls certain signs numbers: in order to guarantee their existence—though of course in an empirical, not in a purely logical or arithmetical way. The actual purpose which all these theories of irrational numbers are intended to serve is that of presenting arithmetic free from all foreign (even geometrical) admixture and grounding it upon logic alone. This goal is surely to be approved, but it is not reached here. If we are not to disdain appeal to the tangibility of signs, we might as well invoke spatial intuition and determine irrational numbers as ratios between lengths.

We see that numerical signs have here an altogether different importance from that assigned to them before the advent of formalistic theories. They are no longer external aids like blackboard and chalk, but are instead an essential constituent of the theory itself.

This question now forces itself upon us: Is calling these signs numbers enough to ensure that they have the properties of the actual numbers which we have previously been accustomed to regard as quantitative ratios?

§ 88

Thomae writes:

> The formal conception of numbers accepts more modest limitations than does the logical conception. It does not ask what numbers are and what they do, but rather what is demanded of them in arithmetic. For the formalist, arithmetic is a game with signs, which are called empty. That means they have no other content (in the calculating game) than they are assigned by their behaviour with respect to certain rules of combination (rules of the game).

The chess player makes similar use of his pieces; he assigns them certain properties determining their behaviour in the game, and the pieces are only the external signs of this behaviour. To be sure, there is an important difference between arithmetic and chess. The rules of chess are arbitrary, the system of rules for arithmetic is such that by means of simple axioms the numbers can be referred to perceptual manifolds and can thus make important contribution to our knowledge of nature.

In other words:

Arithmetic is concerned only with the rules governing the manipulation of the arithmetical signs, not, however, with the reference of the signs. Here we might notice a difference in Heine's standpoint: Thomae rejects the question concerning the nature of numbers, as unimportant for arithmetic, while Heine answers it by saying that numbers are signs. But as both agree that arithmetic has to occupy itself with signs, the difference is unimportant. Heine calls these signs numbers; Thomae, on the other hand, appears to understand by 'number' something whose nature is of no concern to arithmetic and is therefore not a sign but perhaps constitutes the reference of a sign. But as he also speaks of the reference of numbers, he converts numbers into signs again and has no consistent terminology. It is for this reference of the numerical signs, accepted by Thomae but regarded as lying beyond the border of arithmetic, that we have always used the term numbers. Thus we see that these actual numbers or quantitative ratios are to be excluded from arithmetic, according to this mathematician. So we have a peculiar arithmetic here, quite different from that concerned with actual numbers. The one kind of arithmetic we shall call formal, the other kind meaningful. We may take it that Cantor adopts the standpoint of meaningful arithmetic, Heine and Thomae that of formal arithmetic. The distinction cuts deep. However, some future historian may be able to show lack of consistency and thoroughness on both sides—which again somewhat blurs the contrast.

§ 89

What is the reason for preferring the formal to the meaningful? Thomae answers:

The formal standpoint rids us of all metaphysical difficulties; this is the advantage it affords us.

The difficulties spoken of here may well be those met in our examination of Cantor's theory, i.e. of attaining to actual numbers and demonstrating their existence. In formal arithmetic we need no basis for the rules of the game—we simply stipulate them. We do not need to demonstrate that numbers having certain properties exist; we simply introduce figures with rules for their manipulation. We then regard these rules as properties of the pieces, and thus we can—apparently, at any rate—arbitrarily create things having the desired properties. In this way, obviously, we at least save ourselves intellectual labour. Thomae, to be sure, contrasts the arbitrary rules of chess with the rules of arithmetic, the latter causing numbers to make substantial contributions to our knowledge of nature. But this contrast first arises when the applications of arithmetic are in question, when we leave the domain of formal arithmetic. If we stay within its boundaries, its rules appear as arbitrary as those of chess. This applicability cannot be an accident—but in formal arithmetic we absolve ourselves from accounting for one choice of the rules rather than another.

§ 90

Let us try to make the nature of formal arithmetic more precise. The obvious question is 'How does it differ from a mere game?' Thomae answers by alluding to the services it could render to natural science. The reason can only be that numerical signs have reference and chess pieces have not. There is no other ground for attributing a higher value to arithmetic than to chess. But what constitutes the difference lies, according to Thomae, outside arithmetic, which in and for itself has the same value as chess and is more of an art or game than a science. Although numerical signs designate something, this can be ignored, according to Thomae, and we can regard them simply as pieces manipulated in accordance with rules. If their reference were to be considered, this would supply the grounds for the rules; but this occurs behind the scenes, so to speak, for on the stage of formal arithmetic nothing of the sort can be seen.

Now it is quite true that we could have introduced our rules of inference and the other laws of the *Begriffsschrift*[A] as arbitrary stipulations, without speaking of the reference and the sense of signs. We would then have been treating the signs as figures. What we took to be the external representation of an inference would then be comparable to a move in chess, merely the transition from one configuration to another. We might give someone our formulas I to IV and the definitions *A* to *H* of the first volume as starting points—as we might the initial positions of the pieces in chess—tell him the rules permitting transformations, and then set him the problem of deriving our theorem 71 of the first volume, all this without his having the slightest inkling of the sense and reference of these signs, or of the thoughts expressed by the formulas. It is even conceivable that he might solve the problem in just the manner in which we did. It is obvious, of course, that intellectual labour would still be required —as it is for a corresponding chess problem of passing from an initial position to a given final position in accordance with the rules of the game, where there could be no question of thoughts expressed by the various positions, and no move could be interpreted as an inference. Although intellectual labour would thus be expended, there would be wholly lacking that train of thought which accompanied the affair for us and actually made it interesting. It might be possible, but scarcely profitable; refusal to interpret the signs would not simplify the problem but make it much harder.

§ 91

Whereas in meaningful arithmetic equations and inequations are sentences expressing thoughts, in formal arithmetic they are comparable with the positions of chess pieces, transformed in accordance with certain rules without consideration for any sense. For if they were viewed as having a sense, the rules could not be arbitrarily stipulated; they would have to be so chosen that from formulas expressing true propositions could be derived only formulas likewise expressing true propositions. Then the standpoint of formal arithmetic would have been abandoned,

---

[A] The reference is to Frege's formal system, as expounded in the *Grundgesetze*. See also his *Begriffsschrift, eine der arithmetischen nachgebildete Formalsprache des reinen Denkens* (Halle, 1879).

which insists that the rules for the manipulation of signs are quite arbitrarily stipulated. Only subsequently may one ask whether the signs can be given a sense compatible with the rules previously laid down. Such matters, however, lie entirely outside formal arithmetic and only arise when applications are to be made. Then, however, they must be considered; for an arithmetic with no thought as its content will also be without possibility of application. Why can no application be made of a configuration of chess pieces? Obviously, because it expresses no thought. If it did so and every chess move conforming to the rules corresponded to a transition from one thought to another, applications of chess would also be conceivable. Why can arithmetical equations be applied? Only because they express thoughts. How could we possibly apply an equation which expressed nothing and was nothing more than a group of figures, to be transformed into another group of figures in accordance with certain rules? Now, it is applicability alone which elevates arithmetic from a game to the rank of a science. So applicability necessarily belongs to it. Is it good, then, to exclude from arithmetic what it needs in order to be a science?

§ 92

What is actually gained by so doing? To be sure, arithmetic is relieved of some work; but does this dispose of the problem? The formal arithmetician shifts it to the shoulders of his colleagues, the geometers, the physicists, and the astronomers; but they decline the occupation with thanks; and so it falls into a void between these sciences. A clear-cut separation of the domains of the sciences may be a good thing, provided no domain remains for which no one is responsible. We know that the same quantitative ratio (the same number) may arise with lengths, time intervals, masses, moments of inertia, etc.; and for this reason it is likely that the problem of the usefulness of arithmetic is to be solved—in part, at least—independently of those sciences to which it is to be applied. Therefore it is reasonable to ask the arithmetician to undertake the task, so far as he can accomplish it without encroaching on the domains of the other special sciences. To this end it is necessary, above all things, that the arithmetician attach a sense to his formulas; and this will then be so general that, with the aid of geometrical axioms and physical and astronomical observations and hypotheses, manifold applications can be made to these sciences.

This much, it appears to me, can be demanded of arithmetic. Otherwise it might happen that while this science handled its formulas simply as groups of figures without sense, a physicist wishing to apply them might assume quite without justification that they expressed a thought whose truth had been demonstrated. This would be—at best—to create the illusion of knowledge. The gulf between arithmetical formulas and their applications would not be bridged. In order to bridge it, it is necessary that formulas express a sense and that the rules be grounded in the reference of the signs. The end must be knowledge and it must determine everything that happens.

§ 93

Formal arithmetic forsakes this goal. If it is a game with pieces, it no more contains theorems and demonstrations than does the game of chess. Of course there can be theorems in a theory of chess—but not in chess itself. Formal arithmetic knows nothing but rules. However, a theory of formal arithmetic is conceivable, and in it there will be theorems stating, e.g., that we can move from a certain group of figures to another group of figures in accordance with the rules of the game.

Are definitions possible in formal arithmetic? In any case, not those assigning reference to arithmetical signs; for this kind of arithmetic does not consider their reference. In place of definitions we have here the introduction of new figures accompanied by rules for their manipulation. This is all that we are to understand by the expression 'formal definition' in Thomae. In a theory of formal arithmetic, however, proper definitions are possible, but these do not assign reference to figures—since their reference is to be left out of account—but simply explain expressions to be used for the more succinct statement of the theorems of the theory.

The distinction between the game itself and its theory, not

drawn by Thomae, makes an essential contribution towards our understanding the matter. If we encounter theorems in Thomae's exposition, they must be taken to belong to the theory of the game. These theorems only seem to say something about the figures—whose properties are almost wholly unimportant and are used only to identify the figures; the theorems throw light upon the properties of the *rules* of the game. Similarly in the theory of chess it is not the chess pieces which are actually investigated; it is a question of the rules and their consequences.

Formal arithmetic differs from chess inasmuch as new pieces with new rules can always be added, while in chess everything is fixed. This makes us doubt whether a theory of the calculating game is possible. For it might be suspected that there could be no definitive theorems. The introduction of new pieces might render possible much that was previously impossible; and, conversely, much that was previously possible might become impossible. In chess, at any rate, the presence of new pieces would interfere with many moves. It must be proved that something similar does not happen in arithmetic before we can regard the possibility of a theory of the calculating game as assured.

§ 94

The question, 'What is demanded of numbers in arithmetic?' is, says Thomae, to be answered as follows: In arithmetic we require of numbers only their signs, which, however, are not treated as being signs of numbers, but solely as figures; and rules are needed in order to manipulate these figures. We do not derive these rules from the reference of the signs, but lay them down on our own authority, retaining full freedom and acknowledging no necessity to justify the rules; though we exercise this freedom with an eye to possible applications, since otherwise arithmetic would be a game and nothing more.

Accordingly, we can also answer Thomae's question as follows: In the calculating game nothing whatsoever is required of numbers, for here the numerical signs are quite dissociated from their reference (the numbers themselves) and could be replaced by any other figures whatsoever.

§ 95

It might seem that some of Thomae's own words contradict our attempted presentation of his view, according to which numerical signs are treated in formal arithmetic as if they designated nothing. When Thomae says, for example, 'For the formalist, arithmetic is a game with signs which are called empty. That means they have no other content (in the calculating game) than they are assigned by their behaviour with respect to certain rules of combination (rules of the game),' the signs appear to be treated as not wholly empty, a certain content being ascribed to them of which even arithmetic takes account. But this appearance is due to an inaccurate formulation, prompted perhaps by a certain repulsion from empty signs. Can one say that a content is assigned to chess pieces by their behaviour with respect to the rules of chess? I am aware that the chess pieces are given, likewise that rules for their manipulation have been established, but I know nothing of any content. It can surely not be said that the black king, in consequence of these rules, designates something, as, say, the name 'Sirius' designates a certain fixed star. On the contrary, the appropriate way if speaking is to say that the rules of chess treat of the black king.

Moreover, to speak of the behaviour of the signs with respect to the rules seems to me unfortunate. I do not behave with respect to the civil laws simply by being subject to them, but only in obeying or disobeying them. Since neither the chess pieces nor the numerical figures have a will of their own, it is the player or the calculator—and not the pieces or figures—who, by obeying or disobeying the rules, behaves with respect to them. All that remains is quite simply that certain rules treat of the arithmetical figures.

§ 96

When it is added, 'The chess player makes similar use of his pieces; he assigns them certain properties determining their behaviour in the game, and the pieces are only the external signs of this behaviour,' this is not precise. For after all, chess pieces acquire no new properties simply because rules are laid down;

after, as before, they can be moved in the most diverse ways, only some of these moves are in accord with the rules while others are not. Even this accord does not arise from the establishment of the rules; it is only that we are unable to judge of this accord until we know the rules. Nor can I find that a pawn in chess is an external sign of its behaviour; and I always return to the simple expression: the rules of chess treat of the manipulation of the pieces. Would it not be an eccentric way of talking if, instead of saying, 'The Prussian constitution assigns to the king certain rights and duties,' we should say 'The king of Prussia is an external sign of his constitutional behaviour'? I must repeat that the use of expressions such as 'to be an external sign of something,' 'to behave with respect to rules,' only obscure a quite simple matter, without adding to what is said by the sentence, 'The rules of chess treat of the manipulation of the chess pieces.'

Because a rule not infrequently treats of several pieces* and several rules concern the same piece, the relation of a piece to a rule is not at all to be compared with the relation of a sign to its sense or reference. In any case, the rules of a game do not cause a configuration of chess pieces to express a thought; and the corresponding thing is true of the formulas of the arithmetical game.

§ 97

Somewhat later Thomae writes: 'There are however cases in arithmetic where a number† has more than a mere formal reference, e.g. in the sentence, "this equation is of degree 3," etc.'

Accordingly, it appears that in addition to the proper reference of numerical signs (which needs to be considered in arithmetic only in exceptional cases) there is here recognized a formal reference. If this were true there would be danger of ambiguity; but only an unhappily chosen expression is to blame. What should be said is only that in some cases numerical signs can be

---

* The squares of the chessboard must here properly be counted among the pieces.

† The word 'number' here obviously replaces 'numerical sign'; for reference can be spoken of only if this is the case. But above, where the question, 'What are numbers?' was set aside, the reference of numerical signs was obviously meant. In what follows, however, Thomae regularly uses the word 'number' in the sense of numerical sign, or better, *numerical figure*. Where the case is otherwise, I shall so indicate.

treated merely as figures, but occasionally we must go back to their reference. Certainly it is striking that something more than rules of the game can be considered in formal arithmetic or its theory. How is it conceivable that the reference of the chess pieces—which is immaterial to the game—should become important in the theory of chess?

Thomae's admission that even in formal arithmetic numerical signs are not always used simply as figures is damaging to his doctrine. For he thereby admits that the formal standpoint cannot always be consistently affirmed. It is clear that in the calculating game itself the reference of a sign can never be of concern. We can inquire about reference only if the signs are constituent parts of sentences expressing thoughts. Such sentences might occur in the theory of the game; but the highest degree of confusion is caused if in the exposition of the theory of the game we let the pieces of the game also serve as signs having reference. For then the use of these signs would be regulated by their reference, while the game itself is subject to arbitrarily stipulated rules. That the two modes of treatment agree cannot automatically be assumed. To avoid the confusion due to the twofold role of the numerical signs, the numerical signs used in the exposition of the theory of the game (in so far as reference is assigned to them) must receive forms different from those of the mere numerical figures.

§ 98

It may be useful here to discuss signs in more detail, since the assertion of Heine and others that numbers are signs has stamped them as objects of mathematics, lending them an importance which they would not have had as mere aids to thought and communication. Unsteady habits of speech allow misunderstandings to arise so easily that we cannot proceed too carefully, and must not hesitate to say the obvious, in order to be sure of having an agreed starting point.

What are signs? I will limit my considerations to structures created by writing or printing upon the surface of a physical body (blackboard, paper); for clearly only these are meant when it is said that numbers are signs. But we shall not call every such structure a sign—a blot, for instance, would not generally be held worthy of this honour—but only such as serve to express, designate, or assert something. We do not wish to say something about a sign when we use it, but its reference is usually the main thing. For example, an astronomer means the planet Jupiter when he uses its sign '$\u2643$'; the sign itself is really a matter of indifference to him, only an arbitrarily chosen means of expression that is not itself to be considered. The utility of the sign consists in its representative capacity. To be sure, it happens in exceptional cases that we desire to speak of the sign itself—as will occur in our examination of formal arithmetic. In order that no uncertainty shall arise, we must distinguish these two cases by an external mark. The most appropriate procedure is to place the signs, in the latter case, within inverted commas. For greater clarity the word 'sign' can also be inserted. This may seem pedantic but is by no means superfluous. If this distinction had always been kept clearly in mind, perhaps a presentation such as Heine's—whose essence involves equivocation—might never have been possible. Mathematicians commonly use expressions which make such equivocation so usual that it is no longer noticed. Thus we find expressions such as

'Let *a* designate the smallest root of the equation (1),'

and when the letter '*a*' occurs later it is taken to mean the smallest root of the equation in question. Here we have the equivocation. in the first sentence, the sign was meant, but later its reference. We should write either

'Let "*a*" designate the smallest root of equation (1)'

or

'Let *a* be the smallest root of equation (1).'

If required, volumes could be filled with similar examples from the writing of recent mathematicians.* This looks like an unimportant trifle; yet such carelessness seems to be the source of great confusions. And if it can be shown to have furnished the very sustenance of the formalist theory of arithmetic the matter is certainly not to be taken lightly.

* The following example has just come to my notice: 'Concerning the number of different values which a function of given *letters* can acquire through interchanges of these letters.' *Math. Annalen* 33, p. 584.

§ 99

Signs would hardly be useful if they did not serve the purpose of signifying the same thing repeatedly and in different contexts, while making evident that the same thing was meant. This is done by using signs as similar as possible for these different occasions. It is true that it is nearly impossible to reproduce the same shape exactly; and if it were done our eyes are too inaccurate to recognize it with certainty. But it is unnecessary; for if the signs serve only for communication between men (including the case of self-communication, during reflection) only similar signs needs be written, sufficient for the reader to recognize the intention. In what follows we shall understand by 'signs of similar shape' those intended by the writer to have similar shapes in order that they may designate the same thing. Common usage inaccurately calls signs of similar shape one and the same sign, although every time I write an equality sign I produce a different object. These structures differ in their positions, times of origin, and probably in shape. It may perhaps be said that abstraction is made from these differences, so that these figures may be regarded as the same sign. What a lot abstraction is supposed to make possible! Different things cannot be made to coincide by abstraction, and to regard them as the same is simply to make a mistake. If, abstracting from the difference between my house and my neighbour's, I were to regard both houses as the same and disposed of my neighbour's house as if it were mine, the defect of my abstraction would soon be made clear. It may be possible to obtain a concept by means of abstraction, and if we call the extension of a concept 'class' for short, we may reckon all similarly shaped signs in the same class. But this class is not the sign; I cannot produce it by writing —I always produce only individual objects belonging to it. In speaking of the same sign, the coincidence of the reference is transferred to the sign.

§ 100

All this applies to the normal and regular use of signs. In formal arithmetic they play a different role; they are to designate nothing else and are themselves the objects of concern. Occasionally, as in the case of Heine, their tangible character is emphasized and thrown into the scales as evidence. Therefore, we prefer to call them figures, since the purpose of designation is of no concern. Figures will be said to be similar if their differences in shape (which may be perceptible) have no influence on the way they are manipulated according to the laws of the game. In ordinary usage similar signs are supposed to stand for the same thing and are therefore treated in many respects as though identical, because they are considered only as signs with that reference. This reason does not apply to similar figures. We may not treat the white pawns on a chessboard as a single chessman. In constructing the rules and discussing the theory of chess we may not use the word 'pawn,' with the singular definite article, as a proper name; for there are several pawns. While meaningful arithmetic may use such expressions as 'the number one,' or simply 'one,' as proper names, such usage is not permissible in the theory of formal arithmetic, for there are very many figure ones. New figure ones are constantly created and old ones destroyed. It will be possible to say here 'a figure one,' 'several figure ones,' 'all figure ones,' but not 'the figure one,' unless additional specifications are given which unambiguously indicate some particular figure one.

The following difference between formal and meaningful arithmetic may also be noticed. In the latter the word 'one' and the sign '1' stand for the same thing, the non-sensible number one itself; while in the former the term 'figure one,' or the erroneously used 'one,' stands for the concept under which the sign '1' and all signs of similar shape are subsumed.

§ 101

Let us examine Thomae's theory more closely. We read in the second paragraph:

Once the concept of the integer and of counting has been acquired, two arithmetical operations may be introduced simply and naturally as special types of counting, viz. addition and multiplication. By their nature, these can always be performed in the domain of integers. But if inverses for these operations are sought, and the new operations of subtraction and division introduced, these cannot always be performed in the domain of integers.

It seems that we start here from what is known about integers, from connexions grounded in their nature. We must then have deserted the formal standpoint to acquaint ourselves with arithmetical operations, which we then wish transferred to formal arithmetic. Accordingly, the integers here in question are the reference of the numerical signs and not the signs themselves. Certainly, from the formal standpoint, we cannot use addition or multiplication as something involving the numbers themselves; but once we have designated the numbers by numerical signs, the properties of the numbers are mirrored in corresponding properties of the signs, and we obtain procedures in the domain of signs which serve to solve problems arising in the domain of numbers. Such manipulation of signs is here called calculation. The rules of this calculation have their foundation in the nature of the numbers themselves and their relations to one another. We may now, however, completely disregard the reference of the numerical signs, treat them as mere figures, and consider the rules of manipulation as arbitrary rules without demand for justification. And we can now calculate according to these rules, using figures without at all knowing whether they are signs, or whether the rules have any connexion with the reference of these signs.

§ 102

All this follows so directly from the plan for a formal arithmetic in Thomae's sense that no doubt about the correctness of this presentation is possible. But something seems to me to be lacking here, i.e. an indication of what addition, multiplication, subtraction, and division are, in the arithmetical game. In the game of chess we must first acquaint ourselves with the chessmen in order to understand the rules. We expect something similar here. What are the figures to be manipulated? What is the situation before addition and what is it afterwards? And the corresponding things must be known about subtraction; only then can we judge in which cases subtraction is possible. For we must always remember that subtraction is here not a process of thought, but an external activity, an occupation with figures.

Now if subtracting one figure from another consists of writing the latter figure—or one of similar shape—on the left side, and the former on the right side of the subtraction sign, nothing prevents me from subtracting a figure three from a figure two. But I can as easily subtract a calendar symbol for the moon from a calendar symbol for the sun, if I treat these symbols as mere figures. It will then be unnecessary to introduce new figures to make subtraction possible.

We must always bear clearly in mind that a reference is not in question in this arithmetical game. Therefore, we cannot decide whether a subtraction is possible before we know what figures are involved, and what is to be done with them. This must be described for us as exactly as castling is in the game of chess.

How subtraction might be conceived as the inverse of addition we will examine later, after having acquainted ourselves with some rules of formal arithmetic.

At present we have no idea what addition and multiplication are in this calculating game. In any event this addition of numerical signs is quite different from the addition of numbers. If a conqueror burns a city he does not burn the name of the city; what happens to the thing does not automatically happen to its name or sign. Now it may be surmised that to add two numerical signs is to write a third numerical sign that has as reference in meaningful arithmetic the sum of the numbers designated by the first two signs. However, meaningful arithmetic would then be presupposed for all numbers, while it is here assumed known only for positive integers. Otherwise formal arithmetic would be superfluous. Accordingly one would not know what the addition of two numerical figures would be when both of them did not designate positive integers in meaningful arithmetic. We might think of calling a procedure of progress or regress in a row of numerical figures addition, but this too is not of sufficiently general applicability. So perhaps only the following supposition remains: two numerical figures are added by writing two similarly formed signs separated by a plus sign. The same may be said for multiplication, allowing the multiplication sign to stand in place of the sign of addition. According to these explanations all inscribable figures can be added and multiplied, whether they have a reference in any context or not.

§ 103

Thomae writes further:

> However, if one demands that it shall always be possible to perform these operations, one arrives at new numerical structures: zero, the negative numbers, and fractions. These may be conceived as purely formal structures, i.e. as concepts whose content is exhausted by their behaviour with respect to the arithmetical operation.

Here the language hinders understanding. The word 'concept' is obviously not used in our sense, and surely not in the sense that logicians attach to it, for there can be altogether no question of objects to which the concept is applicable. What behaves—to speak in Thomae's way—with respect to the arithmetical operations? Or, as we prefer to say, with what are the rules concerned? Figures, such as might be written in chalk on a blackboard. But these are no more concepts than chess pieces are and belong instead to the domain of physical bodies. Thus we reach the view that these new numerical structures are to be regarded as figures, generated by writing or printing, having no reference or, at least, none that concerns us; rules are, however, provided for their manipulation. There can be no doubt that the *zero*, the *negative numbers*, and the *fractions* of which Thomae speaks are not to be actual numbers in our sense, but numerical figures.

As we have already seen, the standpoint of formal arithmetic by no means requires the introduction of these new numerical figures in order to ensure that subtraction and division can always be performed; yet all the same it will be possible to introduce them.

§ 104

Let us now look at the manner in which Heine handles numbers. He writes:

> The main emphasis is to be put on the arithmetical operations, and the numerical sign must be so chosen, or equipped with such an apparatus, that it may ensure a support for the definitions of the operations.

An enigmatic utterance! If instead of the usual sign for three, I choose to write a capital 'U,' would this, perhaps, less adequately ensure a support for the definitions of the operations? And how can one tell when a sign will ensure such a support? And finally, what is one to understand by the apparatus with which a number sign is to be equipped? Where, for instance, has the sign '3' its apparatus? It might be supposed visible or even tangible, since the number itself is tangible according to Heine.

We notice here a difference between the theories of Heine and Thomae. For according to the latter, the arithmetical operations are already there and the new figures then stand, so to speak, in some kind of relation to them; while for Heine the figures are formed first and the operations, so to speak, are only subsequently defined. The latter method seems preferable; for how can I set up rules without mentioning the figures to which they refer?

Heine further writes:

Rules according to which two numbers joined by the operator sign can be replaced by a single number are called arithmetical operations.

This is obviously expressed awkwardly. One might as well say: The rule according to which one makes socks from thread by means of knitting needles is called the knitting of socks. Heine wants to say: 'Arithmetical operations are substitutions, performed according to certain rules, of a single number in place of a group composed of two numbers separated by an operator sign.'

One may add that the operator sign indicates which rule is to be used. Heine is thinking of a case such as that in which the group '3 + 5' is replaced by the sign '8.' If in a sentence of meaningful arithmetic the group '3 + 5' occurs, we may substitute the sign '8' without changing the truth value, since both signs designate the same object, the same actual number, and therefore everything which is true of the object designated by '3 + 5' must also be true of the object designated by '8.' And in many cases such a substitution will make for an advance in knowledge, because the senses of signs having the same reference may be different, and then the thoughts expressed by the two sentences will be different. The cognitive purpose, therefore, determines the rule that the group '3 + 5' may be replaced by the sign '8.' This purpose requires the character of the rules to be such that if in accordance with them a sentence is derived from true sentences,* the new sentence will also be true. Whether

* More precisely: sentences expressing true thoughts.

the rules satisfy this condition can, of course, be determined only after the signs have been given a reference; for otherwise they cannot be used in sentences expressing true thoughts. This is so for meaningful arithmetic; in formal arithmetic we have rules independent of a sense. Their content is not determined by the cognitive purpose but arbitrarily established.

§ 105

Heine continues:

These rules are so determined that, in the first instance, they yield the results of ordinary calculation when applied solely to the numbers 0, 1, 2, 3, . . . etc.

This is not stated precisely; for the result of ordinary calculation—i.e. surely in meaningful arithmetic—is an actual number, not a numerical sign, and so not a number in Heine's terminology. Heine here borrows from an alien theory. He proceeds:

The impossibility of subtraction in many cases occasions the introduction of new signs or numbers: for each sign a already given, one introduces a new sign $neg(a)$, extending the definitions of the operations appropriately so that they yield results on application to the new numbers and continue to yield the previous results on application to the earlier signs.

Several things must be asked here: First, what is to be understood by 'the impossibility of subtraction'? Apparently it is to mean that the rule is not always applicable, i.e. the rule according to which the result of subtraction is to be that sign which in meaningful arithmetic, limited to non-negative integers, designates the difference. This rule says nothing about what number may be substituted for '3 − 5.' But this does not necessitate the introduction of new signs. One might make the rule that '3 − 5,' just like ' 5 − 3,' should be replaceable by '2.' Since the purpose of these rules is beyond the scope of our considerations, every rule is just as good as any other from our formal standpoint, so long as we avoid a contradiction between rules.

Further, it was said that the definitions of the operations are to be extended. Apparently this is to mean that the rules are to be supplemented.

Heine continues:

It then appears that an appropriate definition of subtraction, $neg(a) = 0 − a$ must hold.

Instead of 'appropriate definition of subtraction,' he should have said 'appropriate stipulation of rules for interchange of figure groups of the form "$a - b$" with other figures.' But we are quite unable to judge what is appropriate, since the purpose is unknown. We do not even know whether such interchange is necessary or whether we might not be satisfied simply with '$3 - 5$.' We are not told how the modified rule is to run; and so a main point remains quite obscure. How can we learn the game, how understand its theory, if the rules are not even presented to us fully? Apparently we are being tacitly referred to our knowledge of meaningful arithmetic. But if we have a knowledge of meaningful arithmetic, we have no need of formal arithmetic.

Next consider the assertion that $neg(a) = 0 - a$ must hold. This is incomprehensible. We have here a group of signs with which no thought is connected; and consequently no assertion can be made. '$neg(a)$' is for us a mere figure and so are the equality sign, the subtraction sign, and the figure zero. Since Heine is here uttering an assertion he intends to express a thought but himself probably doesn't know which. This is the predicament of formal arithmetic: it cannot help but make use of sentences supposed to express thoughts, but nobody can determine exactly what these thoughts are.

We ourselves use the equality sign to express that the reference of the group of signs on the left-hand side coincides with the reference of the group of signs on the right. This is not applicable here, since a reference is not given. But we do not know what else the equality sign is to express. In any case, the signs on the left and on the right must still stand for something and it is to be surmised that we have a theorem from the theory of the game, since neither the reference of figures nor any assertions can come into the game itself.

§ 106

We find something similar in Thomae. There we read:

These rules are contained in the formulas

$$a + a' = a' + a, a + (a' + a'') = (a + a') + a'' = a + a' + a'',$$
$$(a' - a) + a = a'$$
$$aa' = a'a \qquad a(a'a'') = (aa')a'' = aa'a'' \qquad (a':a)a = a'$$
$$a(a' + a'') = aa' + aa''.$$

This is a surprise. What would somebody say if, on asking for the rules of the game of chess, he received no answer—being shown instead a group of chessmen on the chessboard? He would probably say he could find no rules there, since he associates no sense with the chessmen and their positions. The case only seems different here because we already know from meaningful arithmetic the plus sign, the equality sign, and the use of letters; but here we wish to practise formal arithmetic, and hence the question arises whether these signs are to be treated as signs after all or only as figures. In the latter case, it would be inconceivable that a rule could be given by means of the figures. But if they are to be treated as signs they cannot have the same reference as in meaningful arithmetic; for if they did we would have a theorem of meaningful arithmetic and not a rule of formal arithmetic.

§ 107

Although the exposition leaves us in the lurch here, we may still try to see what sense these formulas are supposed to have; we may do so by asking what follows from the sense of these signs in meaningful arithmetic, as regards the manipulation of the signs. Let us for the time being disregard the letters, which are clearly intended to make the rule general, and let us consider the formula

$$\text{`}2 + \tfrac{1}{2} = \tfrac{1}{2} + 2.\text{'}$$

This says in meaningful arithmetic that the sum of 2 and $\tfrac{1}{2}$ is the same as the sum of $\tfrac{1}{2}$ and 2, or that $2 + \tfrac{1}{2}$ is the same number as $\tfrac{1}{2} + 2$. What follows for the signs? Clearly that a group of signs having the same shape as '$2 + \tfrac{1}{2}$' may always be replaced by one having the same shape as '$\tfrac{1}{2} + 2$,' and vice versa. It is of course presupposed here that signs or groups of signs of similar shape always stand for the same. We have thus established the rule of formal arithmetic which corresponds to our theorem of meaningful arithmetic, and we may suppose that Thomae would express this rule by means of the formula '$2 + \tfrac{1}{2} = \tfrac{1}{2} + 2$.' The formula '$a + a' = a' + a$' would then say according to Thomae: A group of figures consisting of one numerical figure to the left and one to the right of a plus sign may be replaced by

a group of figures of the same kind in which the numerical figures
have reversed their position relative to the plus sign. It would
have to be stated in advance which figures are numerical figures.

Let us remember that the theory of the game must be distinguished from the game itself. It is true that the moves of the
game are made in accordance with the rules; yet the rules are
not objects of the game, but the foundation of the theory of the
game. It is true that the moves of chess are made in accordance
with rules; but no position of the chessmen and no move expresses
a rule; for it is not at all the job of chessmen to express anything;
they are, rather, to be moved in accordance with rules. So, if
we regard formal arithmetic as a game, the formula '$a + a' =
a' + a$,' as expression of a rule of the game, is one of the founda-
tions of the theory of the game, upon which inferences belonging
to that theory can be based; but it is not anything which is
changed in the course of the game, not an object of the game,
not comparable with a configuration of chessmen, but rather
with the verbal expression of a rule of chess.

§ 108

Let us ask now what corresponds to a move in chess, what
procedures are controlled by the rules of formal arithmetic.
If we interpret the sense of Thomae's formulas cited above in the
same way as we did in the case of the first formula, we find that
each one permits one group of figures to be replaced by another
group or by a single figure. We can best imagine this by thinking
of the figures as written in chalk on a blackboard. We then, for
instance, erase a group of figures of the same shape as '$2 + \frac{1}{2}$'
and write one of the same shape as '$\frac{1}{2} + 2$' in its place. This
procedure corresponds to a move of chess and is performed in
accordance with a rule of formal arithmetic. From the standpoint
of meaningful arithmetic it may seem trifling even to mention
the chalk, the erasing, in short all this external activity; but let us
not forget that the calculating game consists of just such external
activity.

The erased group of figures will have been part of a larger
group and our memory of meaningful arithmetic leads us to
suppose that the latter group of figures will be something which

we call an equation or an inequation. So from the group shaped similarly to '$(2 + \frac{1}{2}).5 = 12 + \frac{1}{2}$,' say, will arise a group shaped similarly to '$(\frac{1}{2} + 2).5 = 12 + \frac{1}{2}$.' Each one of these corresponds to a position in chess. But we have already learned to recognize equations as expressions of rules. We therefore note that equations play a double role here; first, in the game itself, where, like configurations in a chess game, they express nothing; and secondly, in the theory of the game, where they must express the rules and also, we may suppose, deductions from these rules. Let us try to imagine the corresponding situation in the game of chess. In such a case the rules of the game would be expressed by means of groupings of chessmen, which might also occur in the game itself. General statements would then have to be supplied stating how the chess positions were to be understood as rules or theorems of the theory. In other words, some language would have to be given whose means of expression would be the chessmen and their positions on the chessboard. It might then happen that a position would need to be regarded in two ways: first, in the game itself, where it would express nothing, but would merely have arisen from an earlier position as a result of a move, and might change into another as a result of a further move; secondly, in the theory of the game, where it would be a theorem, and so have a sense. An inference would then appear as a transition to a new position, and the rules in accordance with which such transitions would have to be performed would follow from the logical laws and from the manner in which the chessmen expressed a sense by means of their configuration. These rules, then, could not be stipulated arbitrarily and it could not be expected that they would coincide with the rules of the game of chess. The double role of pieces and the consequent double nature of rules, in the game itself and in its theory, would make insight into the situation so difficult that one would be inclined to think this double role had been purposely invented to cause as much confusion as possible

§ 109

Now we have such a double role of the figures in formal arithmetic. Here too we must first have rules for the manipula tion of figures in the game itself, and these may be constructed arbitrarily with no consideration for any sense. Secondly, we must have rules according to which these same figures are handled in the theory of the game as signs; and these cannot be arbitrary, for they must take account of the sense which the combinations of these signs express in the theory of the game. Now it is a great error not to distinguish between these two systems of rules, but to presuppose their identity without attempting to prove it. Rather must it be supposed in the first instance that the rules of the game lose their validity as soon as the equations are regarded as theorems of the theory of the game and no longer as senseless combinations of figures. The only radical way to bring light into this jungle is not to use the numerical figures and the operator signs (like '+,' '=') in this double manner, but to allow them to appear only in the game itself, while expressing the rules and theorems of the theory of the game in the words of ordinary language. In the following discussions of formal arithmetic an equation is therefore not to express anything, not to have any sense, but is to be considered merely as a group of figures to be manipulated according to the rules of the game. What is called the equality sign in meaningful arithmetic is here only a figure, not standing for a relation.

We have seen that the rules in Thomae's inventory permit the substitution of one figure or group of figures for another. We can thus formulate them in words as we did in the case of the first rule. It seems still more suitable to let Thomae's equations stand as groups of figures from which the game starts, analogous to the initial configurations of the chessmen. Then they express no rules, have no sense whatsoever. We then stipulate the following rule: Given an equation and a formula containing as part a group of signs of the same shape as the group of signs on one side of the equality sign in that equation, it is permissible to substitute for this part of the formula a group of signs of the same shape as the group on the other side of the equality sign.

§ 110

This rule gives permission to do something, as do the rules in chess, where nothing may be done which is not permitted by a rule. One can add rules concerning the interchangeability of letters with each other or with numerical figures. These rules also will permit something. This can really give nobody a liberty he did not previously have; these rules are not established in the name of reason or nature; it is merely that through them some actions become legitimate in the calculating game. There is no question here of truth, as there is in meaningful arithmetic; the arithmetical legislator may regard as legal whatever he wishes, and he is not restrained by considerations of the reference of the figures, since officially they have none for him. The rules of formal arithmetic, as patterns for action, are more closely related to the laws of morality than to the laws of meaningful arithmetic, which can be unrecognized but never broken.

§ 111

When we compare Thomae's rules, or those we offer in their place, with the rules of chess, we notice that they apply to all numerical figures indifferently, while in chess different rules hold for pawns and knights. If there were no other rules in formal arithmetic, there would be no point in using variously shaped numerical figures. If all rules concerning the figure two also applied to the figure three and vice versa, there would be no point in distinguishing these forms. If all chess pieces were treated like pawns, they could all be shaped like pawns.

Looking once more at meaningful arithmetic, we notice that though there are laws applicable to all numbers, it is by no means the case that everything that holds for one number also holds for another. On the contrary, every number differs essentially from every other and hence needs a special sign. If formal arithmetic is not to lose all connection with meaningful arithmetic and the manifold shapes of the numerical figures are not to be an unnecessary burden, the rules introduced by Thomae must be supplemented by others not applicable to all numerical figures, so that to each difference of shape shall correspond a difference in the rules. Such rules will be, for instance, that a group shaped like '$1 + 1$' may be replaced by a figure two, that a group shaped like '$2 + 1$' may be replaced by a figure three, that one may replace a group shaped like '$1 - 1$' by a figure zero, a group shaped like '$\frac{1}{2} + \frac{1}{2}$' by a figure one, etc. Since there is no settled boundary to the domain of the numerical figures, it would seem that the inventory of rules cannot be made definitive. In any case, we should note the striking incompleteness of Thomae's list.

§ 112

When we considered the nature of formal subtraction above, we undertook to regard this operation also as the inverse of addition. Let us do so now. To subtract one figure from another will then mean to write down a third numerical figure, or group of figures, such that any figure group resulting from addition of this third group to the first figure in accordance with the rules of formal arithmetic will be replaceable by a figure of the same shape as the second. Here, addition is the manipulation described in the previous sections. For example, if a figure two is to be subtracted from a figure three, one can use one of Thomae's rules, according to which a figure shaped like '$(3 - 2) + 2$' may be replaced by a figure three. Hence we see that every group of figures shaped like '$3 - 2$' is a solution to the problem. But not only solutions of this form are to be recognized, but also such as have shapes like '$2 - 1$,' and '1,' and very many others. It is true that this does not follow from Thomae's rules; but we have already seen them to be incomplete. We must presuppose rules according to which groups of figures like '$(2 - 1) + 2$' and '$1 + 2$' may also be replaced by a figure three. Accordingly, formal subtraction would be a multivalued operation, as mathematicians say, because the problem of subtraction would permit many solutions. In this respect there would be an essential deviation from meaningful arithmetic, where subtraction is single valued.* If in meaningful arithmetic $3 - 2$ or $2 - 1$ or 1 is offered as a solution of the subtraction problem, we have in mind the reference of the signs, which is the same. If one writes figure ones or groups shaped like '$2 - 1$' on different parts of a blackboard, these all have the same reference; and despite the difference in location and shape of the signs, there is in meaningful

---

* Of course this formal subtraction really corresponds in name only with subtraction in meaningful arithmetic; and the true situation would be clearer if this apparent agreement were avoided by choice of a different word.

arithmetic just one solution. But here in the arithmetical game the figures and groups of figures themselves are solutions and since they differ in location and shape we have many solutions.

One might try to avoid this conclusion by appealing to Thomae's formal reference of number figures. One might say: Because all these figures and groups, presented as solutions, are manipulated according to the same rules, they have the same formal reference; and that formal reference is the actual solution. Against this we may object:

1. The formal reference, as explained above, cannot be recognized.

2. This formal reference, if admissible, would be the same for all numerical figures, at least on the supposition that the rules are Thomae's, which hold indifferently for all numerical figures.

3. No further calculation with the results of subtraction would be possible, since rules of calculation apply to numerical figures and not to their problematic formal reference. In chess we move the chessmen themselves, not a certain something common, say, to all black pawns.

What has been said about subtraction is also essentially applicable to division.

§ 113

Now Thomae comments at the end of No. 2, concerning the arithmetic of integers:

It proves the uniqueness (consistency) of the four basic operations, for all numbers except zero—with which only addition, subtraction, and multiplication but not division can be performed uniquely (i.e. consistently). A quotient whose denominator is 0 has no meaning, and zero occupies a singular position among the numbers.

The arithmetic which proves this must be meaningful, so that nothing is gained for formal arithmetic; for addition, multiplication, subtraction, division in meaningful arithmetic are quite different from the operations bearing the same names in formal arithmetic. The uniqueness of the former is not present in the latter. And there is no reason here for according the figure zeros any special position. At least in Thomae's set of rules the figure zeros are not mentioned particularly, and all numerical figures are treated in exactly the same manner. There is no reason why the group of figures '2:0' or '2/0' might not be the answer to a division problem just as well as '2:3' or '2/3.' In the sentence 'A quotient whose denominator is zero has no meaning,' groups of figures like the ones above are apparently called quotients.* Lack of meaning is no reason for formal arithmetic not to make use of such groups; for it is anyhow not concerned with meaning, and this unconcern is the very reason why it is preferred to meaningful arithmetic. For formal arithmetic, '2/3' has no more meaning than '2/0,' and both groups can be manipulated according to rules equally well.†

What does Thomae really want to say when he denies that a quotient with denominator zero has meaning? Presumably that a group of figures in which a figure zero appears to the right of a colon, or under a division bar, is not permitted. Are we to understand only that the rules of the game do not give permission for such a construction? Or that they expressly forbid it? In the first case we would have a theorem from the theory of the game, analogous, for instance, to the theorem of chess that a bishop standing on a white square cannot land on a black square. There is no prohibition to that effect, but the freedom of movement granted the piece by the rules is not sufficient to accomplish the manoeuvre. But Thomae did give us a rule allowing the appearance of such groups of figures as have here been declared illegitimate. According to this rule it is permissible to substitute for a figure two the group of figures '(2:0).0.' Therefore, if it is permissible to write a figure two, it is, according to this rule, also permitted to write one shaped like '2:0.' If this is nevertheless to be illegitimate, it is not a consequence of one of the rules so far introduced, but needs a prohibition; and our sentence, 'A quotient whose denominator is zero has no meaning,' must then be interpreted either as a prohibitory rule or as a theorem from the theory of the game. If it is the latter, it is a consequence of the rules. Amongst these there must then be at least one prohibitory rule, because no prohibition restricting a permissive

---

* If the quotient were itself a meaning, one could hardly be talking about *its* meaning.

† Formal arithmetic does not seem true to itself here. In fact it sometimes appears as though formal arithmetic is really meaningful arithmetic, which, for the sake of avoiding inconvenient questions, tries to pretend it is formal, without, however, quite bringing it off.

rule can follow from a set of exclusively permissive rules. In any case, there must be at least one prohibitory rule in addition to permissive rules. As in the case of all rules, no reason can be given for such a prohibition except the will of the lawgiver.

§ 114

Another question arises here: Are such groups of figures as '2:(1 − 1),' '2:(2 − 2),' '2:(6 − 2.3)' admissible? Obviously Thomae would deny this. But, it will be objected, this is obvious; 1 − 1 is zero, and so are 2 − 2, and 6 − 2.3. It is true that in meaningful arithmetic '1 − 1,' '2 − 2,' and '6 − 2.3' stand for the same as the sign '0'; but let us not forget that we are considering formal arithmetic. We are concerned here with the groups of figures themselves and not with their reference; and it cannot be denied that they differ amongst themselves, and differ from the figure zero, not only as two pawns of the same colour in chess differ, but also in the manner of different chessmen, say knight and bishop. Now groups of figures shaped like '1 − 1,' and '2 − 2,' etc., may be replaced by figure zeros. This is not stated in Thomae's rules; but we have already seen that they are incomplete. Yet this is no reason for not permitting such groups as '2:(1 − 1).' However, it is true that an inconsistency in the rules would appear; for one would obtain an illegitimate group on trying to replace a group shaped like '1 − 1' by a figure zero. We might here assume a limitation imposed upon the rule of substitution, by means of the prohibitory rules. But clearly Thomae also wants to prohibit groups shaped like '2:(1 − 1).'*

Interpreting Thomae's sentence, 'A quotient whose denominator is zero has no meaning,' as a prohibitory rule, we shall state it better as follows:

'It is forbidden to form groups of figures in which a figure zero, or a group of figures replaceable by a figure zero according to any rule of formal arithmetic, appears to the right of the division sign.'

* The zero figures therefore are not in a singular position in formal arithmetic.

§ 115

Uncertainty results upon attempted application of this rule (or theorem from the theory of the calculating game); for it must be known which groups of figures can be directly or indirectly replaced by a figure zero; and this question cannot be answered with certainty before all the rules of the game have been formulated. And now the question is whether a complete inventory of rules can be given. Antecedently all admissible classes of figures must have been introduced. If replacement of a certain group of figures by a figure zero does not seem possible according to an incomplete set of rules, it may be made possible by a rule yet to be added, so that an admissible group of figures might become inadmissible because of later rules; and on the other hand, if some rules permit the substitution, it is possible that a later prohibitory rule will cancel the permission.

To be safe, one would have to formulate the principle that all prohibitory rules shall have stronger force than the permissive and at least assemble all rules forbidding the replacement of a figure or group of figures by zero, so that every such replacement, not explicitly forbidden would be permitted; or, conversely, one would have to assemble all the rules permitting such a replacement. Both would be difficult to accomplish, because of the tremendous variety of figures and groups of figures. But until this is done our rule is incomplete and therefore inapplicable.

§ 116

The insufficiency of Thomae's inventory of rules appears again in another connexion. For nowhere do they state how one can replace a group of figures consisting of two number figures separated by a subtraction sign. Consequently it is not possible, according to these rules, to replace a group like '$(3 + 2) - 2$' by a figure three, either directly or indirectly. Let us recall how the corresponding theorem is proved in meaningful arithmetic. There, something like the following may be said:

According to definition, $(3 + 2) - 2$ is the number which, increased by 2, yields $3 + 2$. This number is 3; therefore $(3 + 2)$ $- 2$ coincides with 3.

In this argument the uniqueness of subtraction, which, as we have seen, does not hold in formal arithmetic, is essential. Furthermore it is essential that the group of symbols '$(3 + 2) - 2$' has a reference that can be indicated by the definite article ('*the* number which'), and with the demonstrative pronoun ('*this* number'). This also does not apply in the calculating game. One cannot talk here of definitions; for here the minus line is not a sign of subtraction: it has no reference whatsoever; in place of a definition there are rules for the manipulation of this line; and the very rule which would be of use to us is lacking. Therefore, according to Thomae's rules we are not in a position to transform a figure like '$((3 + 2) - 2) - 3$' into one like '$3 - 3$.' Accordingly we could regard the group '$2:[((3 + 2) - 2) - 3]$' as permitted.

According to Thomae's rules it is also not possible to replace the figure group '$(3.2):2$' by a figure three; for there is no rule allowing a group of figures consisting of two number figures separated by a colon to be replaced by something else.

We shall attempt to correct this insufficiency, not by formulating a new rule, but by using the rule stated at the end of § 109, and adding to Thomae's formulas the following two: '$(a + a') - a' = a$' and '$(a.a'):a' = a.$' These too are now groups of figures from which the game starts. There is presupposed here, as elsewhere, a rule stating how letters may be replaced by numerical figures.

§ 117

If we had neglected the prohibition formulated above (§ 114), we could have started with the figure group '$3.0 = 0$' and used the figure group '$(3.0):0 = 3$,' obtained by substituting the appropriate numerical figures in the second of our two new formulas, to obtain the group '$0:0 = 3$'; similarly we could construct '$0:0 = 4$.' From these two we could then go on to derive the group '$3 = 4$.' And this may be the reason for Thomae's assertion that division cannot always be performed uniquely, i.e. consistently.* But here, in formal arithmetic, there is no immediate contradiction. Why should such a group as '$3 = 4$' not be permitted? In meaningful arithmetic it may not appear

---

* The words 'i.e.' are remarkable here, since the extraction of a square root cannot in general be performed uniquely, though no contradiction results.

as a valid formula, because the different reference of the numerical signs must be considered. This reason is irrelevant here. Till now at least no prohibition has been issued against writing a figure group like '3 = 4.' Only when such a prohibition is issued will there arise a contradiction or, better, disagreement among the rules, some of which permit, and some of which prohibit.

§ 118

Now Thomae says in § 2, immediately after his list of rules:

Subtraction and division become addition and multiplication through the introduction of the new numbers. Since all arithmetic recognizes only these *four*, or if one prefers, *two*, operations, new arithmetical structures will be consistent, if they are consistent with respect to the four (or two) basic operations.

It is hard to understand this declaration. In the first place, we may doubt that all arithmetic recognizes only the operations mentioned. The taking of limits, at any rate, does not seem reducible to these operations. Incidentally, to make such a declaration one would have to know the whole of arithmetic, which is impossible, since this science has not been completed and probably never will be.

Furthermore, it is remarkable that consistency is predicated of a figure. It would sound strange if someone suspected a chessman of harbouring a contradiction. But calling to mind Thomae's mode of expression, according to which the circumstance that rules treat, amongst other things, of a particular figure appears as behaviour of this figure with respect to the rules, and according to which again this behaviour is called the content of the figure, we see that a contradiction prevailing among the rules of chess would appear to be transferred to the interior of a chessman. To reach any understanding we will have to transfer the contradiction back again to the rules.

§ 119

Furthermore, we must ask what is to be understood by a contradiction with respect to the basic operations. No doubt Thomae's statement discussed above, asserting that division by zero cannot be consistently performed, should be considered here. According to this, it must be supposed that Thomae regards a figure as inconsistent with respect to an operation when this operation cannot be consistently performed upon this figure. Accordingly, the zero figures would not be consistent with respect to division, and therefore not consistent in arithmetic generally.

Such a contradiction can arise only when the rules applying to a particular class of figures contradict the general rules applying to all numerical figures. Since all of the latter are, according to Thomae's list, permissive, a contradiction has to be feared only if among the particular rules, treating of one class of figures, there also occur prohibitions. This, in fact, occurs with zero figures. But it also occurs elsewhere. For whenever a new class of figures is introduced, it will be necessary to stipulate that these figures may not occur on the left side of an equation whose right side is a zero figure. For instance, consider the introduction of the class of figures shaped like '$\sqrt{2}$.' If we do not know whether an equation like $0 = \sqrt{2}$ is possible, neither do we know whether we may form the group '$2 : \sqrt{2}$;' we therefore do not know whether we may replace a figure two by a group like '$(2 : \sqrt{2}) : \sqrt{2}$.' It does not help if many attempts at constructing an equation like '$0 = \sqrt{2}$,' according to the general rules and the particular rules for figures shaped like '$\sqrt{2}$,' have failed; for many unsuccessful attempts do not prove impossibility, especially when the attempts are not based on a complete list of rules. Similarly, figure groups like '$0 = 1 - \sqrt{2}$,' and countless others, would have to be prohibited.

Whether all these prohibitory rules could be stated as a single rule, or as a small number of rules, is not our concern here. In any case, among the particular rules about figures shaped like '$\sqrt{2}$,' prohibitory rules occur and their consistency with the general rules cannot be inferred from the mutual concord of the latter. Every class of figures to be introduced will require particular rules, including prohibitions. For if exactly the same rules should hold for the new figures as for some class already in use, there would be no reason for choosing a special shape. For instance, if exactly the same rules were to apply to the figures shaped like 'i' as apply to the figure ones, they would be superfluous. But if the rules differ in part, mutual agreement of the rules dealing with the figure ones does not guarantee the same with regard to the figures shaped like '*i*.'

The assertion that formal arithmetic permits of a completely, consistent foundation accordingly lacks proof; on the contrary, its truth is subject to grave doubts. Thomae's contrary opinion rests on the mistaken supposition that the rules given in his second paragraph constitute a complete list and especially on his complete unawareness of the prohibitory rules which each new class of figures necessarily requires.

§ 120

Thomae continues:

Since the further development of the concept of number, in any case, demands at some point the formal viewpoint free of relationships to sensible objects, we decide to adopt this viewpoint already for negative numbers and fractions.

This presupposes that every conception of numbers in which the numbers are not related to sensible objects is a formal conception in Thomae's sense or, expressed conversely, that every meaningful arithmetic relates the numbers to sensible objects. This is an error. In our first volume, nothing could have been further from our mind than treating numerical signs as figures and calling these figures numbers; yet nothing could have been further from our mind also than grounding arithmetic on sense perceptions and calling heaps of sensible things numbers. By the number zero we do not mean a certain round figure; for the latter is only a sign for that which we mean and recognize as existing, although not as a physical body nor a property of such a body. So, however much we agree that arithmetic must beware of any concern with sensible things and that the numerical signs accordingly stand for nothing sensible, we equally emphasize that these signs are not therefore without reference and we decline to call the signs themselves numbers.

§ 121

We turn now to § 3 of Thomae's exposition. There we read:

The rational numbers may be ordered in a series or they may be subsumed under the concept of quantity. It is the case that $3 > 2$ and $3 > -4$ and $9 : 10 > 8 : 9$, because in $9 : 10 = 81 : 90$ the numerator is greater than the numerator 80 in $80 : 90 = 8 : 9$, whereas the denominators are the same.

It is striking that order in a series and subsumption under the concept of quantity are here treated as the same. Is a book therefore a quantity because it can be ordered in a series with other books? Is the manner of ordering of no importance? If so, then everything would actually be quantity, e.g. the strokes of a clock, the letters of the word 'quantity.' We can also order chess pieces in a series; does this make them quantities? One might rather think that the recognition of things as quantities precedes the ordering of them in series and supplies the principle of the order.

In other cases, if things are arranged in series, each thing has at least one neighbour. That seems not to be the case here. This whole passage can only be understood if meaningful arithmetic is known; and then formal arithmetic is superfluous. If we adopt Thomae's formal standpoint, we have no indication of how the numerical figures are to be ordered. Certainly the sign '>' seems to be intended to serve this purpose, but we do not know its reference. The idea of formal arithmetic requires us to conceive it as a figure which—in the calculating game, at any rate—has no reference, but is to be manipulated according to given rules. Nevertheless, such rules are here altogether absent; and this formal conception is self-defeating since '3 > 2' occurs as a component of the declarative sentence 'It is the case that 3 > 2.' It follows that there should be a thought associated with it. Consequently '3 > 2' is not something comparable to a chess position, i.e. something to be transformed in the calculating game. On the contrary, it is a sentence from the theory of the game. For reasons which were developed previously (§ 109), we reject the use of numerical signs here and attempt to express the content in words, in some such way as:

'Each figure three is greater than any figure two,'

where we have ventured to insert the words 'each' and 'any.' The meaning of the words 'greater than' remains to be determined. At any rate, they are not to be taken in a geometrical sense, nor in the sense of meaningful arithmetic; for in the latter we have a relation of numbers themselves, which are the reference of numerical signs—a reference which is not available for formal arithmetic. We do not learn from Thomae the sense of the sentence,

'The numerical figure *a* is greater than the numerical figure *b*.'

We can only surmise that it treats of a relation by means of which the numerical figures are ordered in a series. The nature of this relation and its connexion with the rules of the game remain obscure.

§ 122

Thomae's statement that zero constitutes the limit of a positive number which becomes smaller and smaller is unintelligible from the formalist point of view. So a numerical figure changes in the course of the game? Of its own accord? In some property essential to its manipulation in the game? No more are we able to understand the statements that there is no smallest positive number and that a rational number which is not negative but smaller than any specifiable positive number is necessarily zero. Which zero? There are many zero figures. Is '1 − 1' a zero figure? Immediately there follows the statement:

In this important statement a number, the number zero, is recognized by means of a negative criterion.

The number zero? Which one? 'Zero' is here treated as a proper name. That is correct in meaningful arithmetic, wrong in formal arithmetic. What is a rational numerical figure in the latter? What is a positive numerical figure? A negative numerical figure? The statements cited above will belong to the theory of the game and follow from the rules of the game. How they do so, and from which rules they follow, remains obscure. The words 'rational,' 'positive,' 'negative' designate properties of numerical signs which need consideration in the application of the rules, as do 'white' and 'black' in chess. Small and accidental differences in the form or the colour of the figures—of which the rules do not treat—need no consideration in the theory of the game. We now ask: How do the rules run which do take account of the previously mentioned properties of figures? Which rules make a distinction between positive and negative numerical figures, between rational and irrational? No answer! We see indeed that the formal arithmetician again steps out of his role at this point. The formal conception is a shield held up so long as questions about the reference of the signs threaten. This danger over, the shield is allowed to fall; for it was always a burden.

§ 123

Thomae thinks one can proceed from a given number to even larger and larger numbers, because nothing sets a limit to new constructions by means of addition. Certainly, there is a limit to new constructions, just as to the growth of a city. We have neither an infinite surface nor infinitely many pieces of chalk at our disposal. Numerical figures are diagrams created by writing. An immaterial non-spatial numerical figure is like a castle in the air—but even airy castles are subject to limits. Fantasy lends wings—but even these become exhausted at last.

It may be doubted whether a new construction of numerical figures by means of addition ever occurs. Groups composed of numerical figures and addition signs may so arise, but, since it is nowhere said what a numerical figure is, it remains dubious whether such groups are to be regarded as instances of numerical figures.

We notice that, as in the case of zero, Thomae sees danger of contradiction in the case of the infinite. The rules he himself introduces are all permissive and thus cannot enter into conflict with each other; figures may be freely manipulated in accordance with them, and whether a figure eight stands upright or lies on its side is a matter of indifference so long as there is no special rule applying to the latter case. But here no such rule has yet been introduced.

The infinite is here explicitly called a concept—with no indication of a reason. Why is it not simply a figure? The actual infinite, which G. Cantor rightly defends, is anyhow not a figure, and ought to have no place at all in formal arithmetic.

§ 124

How are irrational numbers introduced into formal arithmetic? At first sight, exactly as in Cantor, to whose fundamental series correspond Heine's number series and Thomae's number sequences. But the members of Cantor's fundamental series are not visible, tangible figures, but rather seem to be of a non-sensible kind, whereas Heine's number series and Thomae's number sequences are obviously meant to be composed of sensible figures. If this interpretation is correct, the similarity between the theories is merely superficial and inessential. Although no clear account of the ordering relation is given by Heine and Thomae, we may suppose them to conceive of it as spatial. We assume that Heine's number series and Thomae's number sequences are groups of numerical figures written side by side from left to right at intervals not too great, each of these figures being called a term of the sequence. We must add that between the individual terms nothing must be visible except empty surface.

We gather from Heine's exposition that such a series is to continue to infinity. In order to produce it we would need an infinitely long blackboard, an infinite supply of chalk, and an infinite length of time. We may be censured as too cruel for trying to crush so high a flight of the spirit by such a homely objection; but this is no answer. If numbers are taken to be tangible figures, whose existence is rendered certain by their tangibility, why then they must be subject to all the limitations of such a material existence. We see that Heine is the victim of a curious fate: the tangibility of numbers, which is supposed to guarantee the existence of numerical series, and consequently of irrational numbers, is in fact just what makes their existence impossible.

Heine now lays down the requirement that a sign shall be allocated to every number series and says:

The series itself, put in square brackets, is introduced as the sign; thus, e.g., the sign belonging to the series a, b, c, etc., is [a, b, c, etc.].

In order to make use of this one must first invent the art of putting an infinite series between brackets.

Heine adds the following definition:

A general number or numerical sign is the sign belonging to a numerical series.

According to this, a numerical series placed within brackets (providing there is such a thing) would be a general number.

We see from this that the real object of Heine's consideration is the numerical series, not in its original nakedness, but dressed up in square brackets.*

§ 125

Thomae tries to avoid the difficulty for formal arithmetic of a series extending to infinity by offering a definition of infinite sequence. He says in § 5:

A sequence of (in the first instance rational) numbers $(a_1 \, a_2 \, a_3 \, . \, . \, a_n \, . \, .)$ is called an infinite sequence if no term in it is the last; so that in accordance with a given prescription new terms and more new terms can always be constructed.

If we did not know what Thomae was trying to say, we might think of a circular ordering of numerical figures. Since that obviously is not intended, a sequence of numerical figures must always have two ends and one term will always be the last. On account of the last part of the above definition (after the semicolon), however, it is to be assumed that 'last' is not to be understood here in its customary sense. I write below a number sequence:†

$$2 \quad 3 \quad 5$$

and ask: Is this infinite according to Thomae? If the figure two is called the first term, then according to ordinary usage of language the figure five will be called the last. Hence we would have no infinite sequence. The emphasis in Thomae's definition, however, is upon possibility. The figure five is not the last term, according to Thomae, since in accordance with a given prescription new terms and more new terms *can* always be constructed. But new terms and more new terms need not actually be constructed. The possibility is enough; the sequence need never contain more than those three terms and would still be infinite so long as that possibility existed. Does the possibility exist? For an almighty God, yes; for a human being, no. We encounter here the difficult concept of the possible, but we can see in any case that the answer to our question is indepen-

* Moreover, the occurrence of the definite article before 'sign belonging to a numerical series' is striking; for various signs may be assigned to the same numerical series, a possibility which Heine also makes use of.

† In what follows let it be called the sequence S. It is to be the example underlying the considerations that follow.

dent of the character of the terms composing the sequence. For sequences are not thereby divided into finite and infinite ones; all become finite or else all infinite, depending upon the sense which is attached to 'can.' We have a similar case in a row of houses gradually extending from a city into the country-side. We can give the definition: 'A row of houses is called an endless row if no house of the row is the last, so that in accordance with a given prescription new houses and more new houses can always be built.' If we presuppose human ability and understand the word 'always' in the strictest sense, no row of houses will then be endless. With the same presuppositions and for the same reason no sequence of numerical signs is infinite. For we see in advance that the possibility of continuing will some time cease.

We see indeed how futile it is to use a definition to deceive ourselves about the limitations of our capacities.

§ 126

But for what purpose do we need infinite number sequences? An answer to this question may show more clearly what we are to understand by this expression. Thomae writes:

A sequence $(\delta_1 \delta_2 \delta_3 . . \delta_n . .)$, is called a null sequence: the number zero is associated with it by means of the equality sign

$$0 = (\delta_1 \delta_2 \delta_3 . . \delta_n . .),$$

if the numbers $\delta_1 \delta_2 . . \delta_n . .$ become as small as we please with increasing subscripts, so that for any number σ, however small, an n can be found such that all terms $\delta_n \delta_{n+1} \delta_{n+2} . . .$ are smaller than σ in absolute magnitude.

The notation is confusing here. We do not yet know, for example, what a subscript within a numerical sequence is. It is true that we can see subscripts within the structure '$(\delta_1 \delta_2 \delta_3 . . \delta_n . .)$,' but this combination of letters, ciphers, dots, and brackets is not a numerical sequence.

We shall surely not go astray if we understand by the subscript of a term an ordinal number indicating the place which this term has in the sequence. The n of which Thomae speaks in his exposition thus proves to be not a numerical sign but rather a number. Let us assume that we had found a case where such an n was $9^{(9^9)}$! Ought we then to use the words 'the $9^{(9^9)}$th term of the sequence S'? Not before we know that the series contains $9^{(9^9)}$ terms. Otherwise 'the $9^{(9^9)}$th term of the sequence S' is a proper name devoid of reference, because a $9^{(9^9)}$th term pre-supposes a $(9^{(9^9)} - 1)$th. In this connexion it is to be noted that terms which are not written down do not exist, for terms are numerical signs, i.e. structures created by writing. But could we not speak of the $9^{(9^9)}$th term of the sequence S by adding 'providing it were to exist'? Yes, just as of the oldest man who lives at latitude one hundred degrees north, providing he were to exist. One might spin interesting fables about him, but they would have no place in science.

Therefore if Thomae understands by 'δ_n,' the nth term of a sequence, he passes into the realm of fiction as soon as the number n is so large that the existence of so many terms cannot be assumed with certainty.

When the discussion concerns a number σ, however small, we must remember that 'number' here means the same as 'numerical figure,' that upon the whole earth only a finite set of numerical figures exist, and that we cannot alter that fact by writing new ones. It is no good pointing to infinitely many possible numerical figures; for only actual figures *are* numerical figures. A merely possible figure is no figure at all. Perhaps we have an idea of a numerical figure and hold that it is possible to write such a figure down; but then we have only an idea, not a figure. Furthermore, it is very doubtful whether it is possible to construct infinitely many numerical figures. Therefore there can be no question here of an unlimited approximation to the null figure, even if we were to accept a relation between numerical figures designated by the words 'smaller in absolute magnitude than.'

§ 127

Thomae makes the following remark about the word 'all':

Since all terms cannot be written down, we are to understand by 'all' here, as in similar cases, the terms, no matter how many, which one might construct; or, to speak negatively, from a certain subscript onward, no term is $> \sigma$.

In this connexion one thing must be remembered. The null sequences are doubtless to be infinite; i.e. it should be possible to construct, i.e. to write down, more and more new terms. But here it is said that not all the terms can be written down. From this is to be inferred that a null sequence, according to Thomae, consists first of terms which are written down, secondly of terms which are not written down but can be written down, and thirdly (so it appears) of terms which cannot be written down. Analogously, an endless row of houses, say, would consist first of houses which are built, secondly of houses that are not built but could be built, and thirdly of houses which neither are built nor could be built. Such a row of houses, beginning in the actual, would therefore extend through the realm of the merely possible into that of the impossible. A remarkable row of houses!

§ 128

Has not the formal arithmetician at this point again become unfaithful to his plan? We know how easy it is to do so, since we are already accustomed to regarding numerical figures as numerical signs, i.e. as proper names designating something. For this reason the example of the houses has such a liberating effect, because the association with meaningful arithmetic here disappears, while on the other hand there is no difference relevant to our question; for both houses and numerical figures are products of purposive human activity, and that alone is the important thing. One might indeed use the houses themselves in place of the numerical figures. Building would correspond to inscribing, demolition to erasing. Inscribing and erasing are indeed the moves in the calculating game. Thus one might easily adapt all the rules of the game to the new case.

In meaningful arithmetic, there is nothing strange about saying that not all the terms of a sequence can be written down; for *signs* of the terms are written. The terms themselves are not created by writing nor is their condition disturbed by writing or not writing. Quite otherwise in the calculating game! Here the numerical figures themselves are the terms. Numerical figures which have not been written no more exist than houses which have not been built. If only three terms have been written, the sequence consists of only three terms. How is it possible to add that not all the terms of the sequence can be written? What can a numerical sequence in the calculating game be other than a whole, a group, consisting of written figures? If such a group cannot be written down, then it cannot come to exist. And since such numerical sequences do not exist eternally, there are none at all and there will be none. If, however, a numerical sequence is written, then all its terms are written; for only in them does it have its being.

In his remark Thomae uses the expression 'terms, no matter how many, which one might construct.' If 'might construct' were replaced by 'has constructed and will construct,' there would be no objection to be made. Terms, however, which are only possible but will never be written are not terms in formal arithmetic.

Numerical sequences are in no more danger of being continued indefinitely than trees are of growing up to heaven. Each will some time reach its greatest length. Let us consider our sequence S at that instant. Let the number of its terms be n; let the $(n - 1)$th term be a figure two, the nth a figure one. We shall then perhaps be able to say: All the terms following the $(n - 2)$th are smaller than the figure three; similarly: All the terms following the $(n - 1)$th are smaller than the figure two; and finally: All the terms following the nth are smaller than the figure one—for no further terms will follow the nth. We can also say negatively: No term following the nth is greater than a figure one. Accordingly our sequence would be a null sequence. We would of course have the same right to say: No term following the nth is smaller than a figure nine. For since no terms at all follow the nth, there are also none of them smaller than a figure nine.

This is how Thomae's words, taken strictly, would have to be understood; but clearly they are not intended to be understood in this way.

§ 129

Let us consider the following case. Let a prescription P be given for prolonging our sequence S. Now let us assume that without knowing anything about the future length of our sequence we can deduce the following statement from the character of the prescription: All terms, if there should ever be any, which are written down according to our prescription and are characterized by having a subscript greater than a hundred, will be smaller than a figure one. If such a statement may be deduced for each positive number figure σ instead of the figure one, with perhaps some other number replacing the number one hundred, Thomae will surely declare the sequence to be a null sequence.

We must always bear in mind, however, that the set of positive numerical figures is finite and will always remain so.

We note further that the possibility of such deductions depends mainly upon the prescription, which however is not at all determined by visual inspection of the sequence S. The above would justify a definition of a null prescription rather than a null sequence.

§ 130

But even a null prescription could not be so defined. We cannot use as a defining characteristic the circumstance that the statement 'All terms formed according to prescription P and having a subscript greater than a hundred are smaller than a figure one' follows from the nature of the prescription P. It might work, however, if the statement followed in an altogether formal way, somewhat as 'There is a B' follows from 'A is a B,' quite independently of what 'A' and 'B' stand for, and on the mere assumption that these signs stand for something. But that is obviously not the case here. The reference of the words 'to be smaller than' in the theory of the calculating game, though unknown to us, must nevertheless be considered here; and propositions must be used indicating the nature of this relation, propositions which, to be sure, we do not know, but whose validity we must assume. We may also have to supply propositions giving more precise information concerning the objects, concepts, and relations mentioned in the prescription. And these propositions will perhaps refer to other objects, concepts, and relations which in their turn will make the introduction of other propositions necessary. Perhaps the proposition to be proved will itself occur among them.

Therefore, since the prescription alone is insufficient and we cannot precisely specify which other propositions are to be introduced, it really makes no sense to say that such and such follows from the prescription. Therefore, we must abandon as a means of definition the use of the circumstance that a proposition follows from the prescription P. For this purpose we can use only the actual proposition that, let us say, for every positive numerical figure σ there is a subscript n such that a term of a sequence is smaller than σ if it is constructed according to the prescription P and if its subscript is greater than n.

But a hypothetical thought is always true if the antecedent is never realized. Thus one can truthfully assert: If a man has lived without food for a thousand years, his hair turns green. So it is no help in defining the null sequence to say what takes place under conditions which have not been and never will be realized.

§ 131

We recognize here the incorrigible disparity between what the introduction of irrationals demands and what formal arithmetic can offer. To introduce irrationals, we need infinitely many numbers; but the numerical signs of formal arithmetic are only a finite set. No definitions, no amount of turning and twisting can change this. In fact, Thomae presupposes infinitely many terms of his sequences inasmuch as he uses signs such as 'δ_n', without an upper limit for n, to represent proper names which have reference, although in infinitely many cases there is nothing to be designated by such a sign.

If an infinite numerical sequence consists of numerical figures and nothing else, if numerical figures are structures produced by writing, then such a numerical sequence can be written down. Let it be done! What will be the result? A series which begins with a figure and ends with a figure. Now a definition may be given according to which the sequence so inscribed is infinite; but what is the use of it? We still fail to get the infinity which we need for the introduction of irrationals. What use is the word 'infinite' when the thing which matters is lacking?

Since actuality is not sufficient, the appeal to possibility, or even impossibility, is in vain, as we have seen. If merely possible figures could be a substitute for actual ones, we would not need the actual figures.

This situation is disguised by the fact that meaningful arithmetic is constantly, though involuntarily, used as a supplement.

In fact, it gleams everywhere so distinctly through the husk of
formal arithmetic that we often think we see it alone. We
forget, however, that much having good reason in meaningful
arithmetic is unjustified in formal arithmetic. We constantly
forget the profound differences. Many a reader has perhaps
condemned our references to time as wholly unmathematical—
when, for example, we assumed that the length of a sequence
changes in time. This complaint would be quite justified from
the standpoint of proper or meaningful arithmetic; in formal
arithmetic, however, time is involved by the subject itself. For
while the actual numbers are timeless, numerical figures arise
and pass away in time. The manipulations of the game also take
place in time.

§ 132

Thomae writes:

The simpliest null sequence is naturally (o o o . . o . .).

Our question is: Does this group of figures designate a
numerical sequence, or is it itself a numerical sequence? According to the usual usage of signs, the first alternative would be
correct; but since the figure zeros are not signs in this context,
but just figures, we must conclude that Thomae intends the
above group of figures to be a numerical sequence. Is this really
so? We have so far assumed that the numerical sequences consist
of numerical figures and nothing else; but here we also see dots
and parentheses. The latter may perhaps be dismissed as mere
drapery. But what have the dots to do with the numerical
sequence? Are they to represent figure zeros? But then why do
not the figure zeros themselves appear? That would be simpler.
We should then have a sequence consisting of eight figure zeros.
But whether we would then have a null sequence in Thomae's
sense is questionable. The alternative is not a sequence of
numerical figures, but a row composed partly of numerical
figures and partly of dots. Only the group made up of the first
three figure zeros can be regarded as a numerical sequence;
the fourth figure zero may not be taken as part of the sequence,
for it is separated by dots. Do the dots invite us to imagine

indefinitely more figure zeros? Mental images of figure zeros are not figure zeros; and an image of an indefinite number of figure zeros is at any rate very vague. Then the whole group of figures would not be presented for its own sake, like a group of chessmen, but the mental images it arouses would be the main thing. We should then again have something like a sign. But would the image belonging to the above group of signs be a null sequence? Would it consist of numerical figures? Hardly! No matter how we twist or turn, we cannot reach an interpretation of our group of figures compatible with the basic idea of formal arithmetic.

§ 133

The affair becomes even harder when we have letters with subscripts in place of numerical figures. Nothing is said about the use of letters in formal arithmetic, although it will deviate from that of meaningful arithmetic. How, for example, are we to interpret the group of letters with subscripts occurring in the following sentence: 'A sequence taken, at first, to consist of rational numbers $(a_1 \, a_2 \, a_3 \, .. \, a_n \, ..)$ is called an infinite sequence'? This is reminiscent of phrases like 'a general, Caesar.' Here 'Caesar' is a proper name, and one could take '$(a_1 \, a_2 \, a_3 \, .. \, a_n \, ..)$' as the proper name of a numerical sequence. But obviously no specific sequence is supposed to be designated. And neither is the group itself a numerical sequence. One may now suppose that it merely indicates a sequence, just as a number is indicated by the phrase 'a prime number p.' Here the letter is not a proper name, but it supplants one. Letters are written instead of proper names for the sake of generality. But it is always possible to get to a particular case by replacing the letters by proper names; for instance, in place of the letter 'p' one puts the proper name '7.' Note well: the proper name, not the figure! Following this method in our particular case, and regarding 'a_1' 'a_2,' etc., as representatives of proper names of numerical signs, we obtain, upon proceeding to a particular case, say '$(3 \, 7 \, 1 \, .. \, 2 \, ..)$,' where every numerical sign designates a number. Of course it will still be unclear what the whole thing is to designate, because no explanation is given of the reference of such a conjunction of signs. In any case we would be in the domain of meaningful arithmetic. But even if we erroneously took the numerical signs as figures, the whole group of figures would not designate a number sequence, nor would it be one (as we saw above).

It follows that we do not reach a satisfactory conception of '$(a_1 \, a_2 \, a_3 \, . \, . \, a_n \, . \, .)$' by analysing it into its constituents. We will therefore be forced to accept it without considering its composition. But then a single letter will serve just as well, and we will be able to say 'a number sequence S,' just as we say 'a prime number p.'

§ 134

Thomae continues in § 5:

To such a sequence we allocate a sign, and this allocation is expressed by the equality sign:

$$'a = (a_1 \, a_2 \, a_3 \, . \, . \, a_n \, . \, .).'$$

We have already seen that this allocation of a sign is a particularly important step in G. Cantor's work; it is also to be found in Heine. The letter 'a' on the left-hand side obviously represents a proper name. But so does the right-hand side. We can replace the right-hand side by a single letter 'S,' as we did above, obtaining

$$'a = S.'$$

To obtain a particular instance we must substitute a proper name both for 'S' and for 'a.' But in that case we shall already have a proper name for the sequence under consideration, viz. the one substituted for 'S,' and we no longer need to assign a further name to the sequence.

Let us consider a particular case. Proceeding from left to right, we chalk a figure two, figure three, and figure five on a blackboard. Let us assume that we have now produced something which would be an infinite number sequence according to Thomae. To enable us to say something about this sequence we assign to it an inverted roman A, '$\forall$,' as a sign, or proper name; we can now say, for example: 'The sequence $\forall$ consists of one figure two, one figure three, and one figure five.' If, for some purpose or other, we want to allot another sign to this sequence, there is nothing to stop us, and we may for instance write,

$$\text{'}\mathfrak{B} = \forall\text{'}$$

where the equality sign stands for coincidence, or identity, or, in other words, what we call equality. This equation follows from Thomae's equation

$$\text{'}a = (a_1 \, a_2 \, a_3 \, . \, . \, a_n \, . \, .)\text{'}$$

as a result of replacing the signs on the left- and right-hand sides, which merely indicate proper names, by proper names. It is of course unlikely that this satisfies Thomae's intention. More likely, he would tell us to write an equality sign to the left of our sequence and, to the left of that, our sign '$\forall$'; so that there would result a group of signs and figures of the form:

$$\text{'}\forall = 2 \; 3 \; 5\text{'}$$

And this, he might say, assigns the sign '$\forall$' to our sequence. This would of course be untenable. First, the left-hand side of the equation '$a = (a_1 \, a_2 \, a_3 \, . \, . \, a_n \, . \, .)$' would be treated quite differently from the right-hand side. On the left-hand side a proper name '$\forall$' would have been substituted for 'a,' while on the right-hand side we substituted the object (the sequence) itself. This violates all the fundamental rules governing the use of letters in mathematics. And a strange mixture of signs and figures would result. The equality sign would be used neither as a mere figure in the game, nor in the manner in which Thomae uses it in the theory of the game, nor yet in the way it is used in meaningful arithmetic; rather, it would indicate that the sign on the left-hand side, '$\forall$,' is to designate the sequence standing on the right-hand side. It would not be correct to interchange the left- and right-hand sides of the equation; for if the sequence were on the left, and '$\forall$' on the right, then the sequence would be presented as a sign for the figure '$\forall$,' which is something quite different.

Whether or not we have hit upon Thomae's meaning, it is certainly not permissible to play around so arbitrarily with the equality sign, as though it had never been used before.

§ 135

The following sentences seem to confirm that we have interpreted Thomae correctly:

For this sign a we sometimes take a rational number. Namely, in those cases in which after a certain term a number constantly recurs, so that

$$a_{n+1} = a_{n+2} = a_{n+3} = .. = a.$$

We then choose the number a as a sign for the sequence. But also in those cases in which the terms of a sequence $(a_1\, a_2\, a_3\, .. \, a_n\, ..)$ differ respectively from the terms of the sequence $(a\, a\, a\, .. \, a\, ..)$ only by the terms of a null sequence (to be defined immediately) we also assign the number a to the sequence $(a_1\, a_2\, .. \, a_n\, ..)$ by means of an equality sign.*

In opposition, we must remember that different things are hereby allocated the same sign, which is contrary to all principles of symbolism. This is however concealed by our recollections of meaningful arithmetic. There glimmers here the thought that all these sequences determine the same number in our sense of the word, the same quantitative ratio—in a manner which can however not be indicated here, for that would demand that the question 'What is a quantitative ratio?' be answered first. When Thomae allocates a sign a to the sequence, his real intention, of which he is not fully aware, is apparently to assign the sign to that quantitative ratio, and then the univocality of the sign would indeed be assured. This ceremonious assignment of signs is to be a substitute for what is really wanted, i.e. a definition of quantitative ratios, and the proof that there are such things. There is no fruit; so we are offered the empty husks instead.

§ 136

What is most surprising is that the programme of formal arithmetic here completely comes to grief, for the numerical figures are used as signs after all. If we tried to create confusion we could hardly do better. For, after all, the central tenet of formal arithmetic is that the numerical figures are mere figures, and not signs. For figures, arbitrary rules could be stipulated, but in the case of signs the rules follow from what they stand for.

---

* What does the equality sign mean in

$$`a_{n+1} = a_{n+2} = a_{n+3} .. = a\,'?$$

Now the question arises whether the numerical figures appearing as terms in a sequence are to be regarded as signs, themselves standing for further sequences. In that case the sequence of which they are terms must itself stand for something; but what? Always to regard the terms of a sequence as signs for another sequence would produce an infinite regress. Accordingly it must be presumed that when numerical figures are used as terms they are not to be regarded as signs. But it is doubtful whether such a distinction is possible. In any case this double usage of similarly shaped structures would be dangerous.

§ 137

It will be unnecessary to contine the examination of Thomae's theory. This attempt at formal arithmetic must be considered a failure, since it cannot be pursued consistently. In the end numerical figures are used as signs after all. Thomae's own inventory of rules of play is incomplete, and we were forced to suppose that such a list could never be completed, for in addition to the permissive rule, prohibitory rules would also have to be established, leading to uncertainty concerning what is permitted—an uncertainty which apparently could never be wholly removed. We tried to remove as much as possible the confusion resulting from lack of distinction between the game itself and the theory of the game. But it did not seem possible to give a theory of the game before all the rules had been presented. We saw that terms and expressions were borrowed unconsciously and without explanation from meaningful arithmetic (e.g. 'larger than' and 'smaller than') and that their role in the calculating game remained obscure, although it seemed to be highly important. Formal arithmetic proved unable to define the irrational, for it had only a finite number of numerical figures at its disposal.

Many mathematicians are unclear about the import of the fundamental thought of formal arithmetic. Essentially, it seems to be regarded as meaningful arithmetic relieved of the need to supply reference for the signs. In fact, the conception of numbers as figures is really used only at the outset, where that obligation is oppressive. Later one slides back unawares into meaningful arithmetic. And yet this formal conception has consequences which can be burdensome; so completely does it change arithmetic, from its very foundations up, that it hardly seems admissible to use the name 'arithmetic' for the formal as well as the meaningful study. Formal arithmetic can remain alive only by being untrue to itself.* Its semblance of life is facilitated by the haste with which mathematicians usually hurry over the foundations of their science (if indeed they have any concern for them), in order to reach more important matters. Many things are omitted completely, others briefly touched on, nothing performed in detail. Thus a theory may appear secure which would immediately reveal its weaknesses upon any serious attempt at consistent elaboration. This shows the road to refutation. We need only follow the lines of thought further, to see where they lead. To take formal arithmetic seriously is to overthrow formal arithmetic; and that is what we have done.†

* A fancier of paradoxes might say: the correct interpretation of the formal theory consists in interpreting it incorrectly.

† H. v. Helmholtz apparently adheres to a formal theory in his essay 'Zählen und Messen erkenntnistheoretisch betrachtet' (*Philos. Aufsätze Ed. Zeller zu seinem 50-jähr Doktorjubiläum gewidmet*) when he says, e.g., 'I regard arithmetic, or the theory of pure numbers, as a method founded on purely psychological facts, which teaches us the consistent application of a system of signs (namely numbers) of unlimited extension and unlimited possibilities of refinement. Arithmetic investigates which combinations of these signs (arithmetical operation) lead to the same end product.'

Here, too, the signs are endowed with magical powers because their reference has disappeared. To add to the confusion, psychology and empiricism are dragged in. Helmholtz is out to found arithmetic empirically, whether it bends or breaks. Consequently he does not ask: How far can one get without using facts of experience? but he asks: How can I most rapidly introduce some experiential facts? All who have this desire succeed very easily by confusing the application of arithmetical theorems with the theorems themselves. As though the questions about the truth of a thought and its applicability were not quite different! I can very well recognize the truth of a proposition without knowing whether I will ever have a chance to make use of it. But just make a fine mixture of everything! Never mind distinguishing things that are different! And clarity will come of its own accord. I have hardly ever seen anything less philosophical than this philosophical essay, and hardly ever has the sense of the epistemological problem been more misunderstood than here.

FREGE ON RUSSELL'S PARADOX

Grundgesetze der Arithmetik, Vol. ii, Appendix, pp. 253-65

HARDLY anything more unfortunate can befall a scientific writer than to have one of the foundations of his edifice shaken after the work is finished.

This was the position I was placed in by a letter of Mr. Bertrand Russell, just when the printing of this volume was nearing its completion. It is a matter of my Axiom (V).[A] I have never disguised from myself its lack of the self-evidence that belongs to the other axioms and that must properly be demanded of a logical law. And so in fact I indicated this weak point in the Preface to Vol. i (p. VII). I should gladly have dispensed with this foundation if I had known of any substitute for it. And even now I do not see how arithmetic can be scientifically established; how numbers can be apprehended as logical objects, and brought under review; unless we are permitted—at least conditionally—to pass from a concept to its extension. May I always speak of the extension of a concept—speak of a class? And if not, how are the exceptional cases recognized? Can we always infer from one concept's coinciding in extension with another concept that any object that falls under the one falls under the other likewise? These are the questions raised by Mr. Russell's communication.

Solatium [sic] *miseris socios habuisse malorum.* I too have this comfort, if comfort it is; for everybody who has made use in his proofs of extensions of concepts, classes, sets,* is in the same position as I. What is in question is not just my particular way of establishing arithmetic, but whether arithmetic can possibly be given a logical foundation at all.

But let us come to the point. Mr. Russell has discovered a contradiction which may now be stated.

---

* Herr R. Dedekind's 'systems' also come under this head.

[A] Vol. i, § 3, § 20. Cf. also Frege's *Function und Begriff* for an explanation of the ideas used; especially pp. 9–10, 18. For any (first-level) function of one argument, there is some object that is its *value-range*; and two such functions are by Axiom (V) equal in value-range if and only if their values always equal for any given argument. Concepts (ibid., pp. 15–16) are functions whose values can only be the True or the False. For the value-ranges of concepts, which are called their *extensions*, the principle runs thus: Two concepts are equal in extension if and only if whatever falls under either falls under the other.

Nobody will wish to assert of the class of men that it is a man. p. 254] We have here a class that does not belong to itself. I say that something belongs to a class when it falls under the concept whose extension the class is. Let us now fix our eye on the concept: *class that does not belong to itself.* The extension of this concept (if we may speak of its extension) is thus the class of classes that do not belong to themselves. For short we will call it the class K. Let us now ask whether this class K belongs to itself. First, let us suppose it does. If anything belongs to a class, it falls under the concept whose extension the class is. Thus if our class belongs to itself, it is a class that does not belong to itself. Our first supposition thus leads to self-contradiction. Secondly, let us suppose our class K does not belong to itself; then it falls under the concept whose extension it itself is, and thus does belong to itself. Here once more we likewise get a contradiction!

What attitude must we adopt towards this? Must we suppose that the law of excluded middle does not hold good for classes? Or must we suppose there are cases where an unexceptionable concept has no class answering to it as its extension? In the first case we should find ourselves obliged to deny that classes are objects in the full sense. For if classes were proper objects, the law of excluded middle would have to hold for them. On the other hand, there is nothing 'unsaturated' or predicative about classes that would characterize them as functions, concepts, or relations. What we usually consider as a name of a class, e.g. 'the class of prime numbers,' has rather the nature of a proper name; it cannot occur predicatively, but *can* occur as the grammatical subject of a singular proposition, e.g. 'the class of prime numbers contains infinitely many objects.' If we were going to dispense classes from the law of excluded middle, we might think of regarding them (and, in fact, value-ranges generally) as improper objects. These could then not be allowed as arguments for all first-level functions. But there would also be functions that could have as arguments both proper and improper objects. At least the relation of equality (identity) would be a function of this sort. (An attempt might be made to escape this by assuming a special sort of equality for improper objects. But that is certainly ruled out. Identity is a relation given to us in such a specific form that it is inconceivable that various kinds of it should occur.)

But now we should get a great multiplicity of first-level functions.[B] First, there would be those that could have only proper objects as arguments; secondly, those that could have both proper and improper objects alike as arguments; lastly, those that could have only improper objects as arguments. There would also come about another division of first-level functions, on the p. 255] basis of their values. Here we should have to distinguish first, functions that had only proper objects as values; secondly those that had both proper and improper objects alike as values lastly, those that had only improper objects as values. First-level functions would be divided in both ways simultaneously; we should thus get a ninefold division of types (*Arten*). To these again there would correspond nine types of value-ranges—o improper objects—between which we should have to draw logical distinctions. Classes of proper objects would have to be distinguished from classes of classes of proper objects; extension of relations[c] holding between proper objects would have to be distinguished from classes of proper objects, and from classes o extensions of relations holding between proper objects; and so on. We should thus get an incalculable multiplicity of types and in general objects belonging to different types could not occur as arguments of the same function. But it appears extraordinarily difficult to set up a complete system of rules for deciding which objects are allowable arguments of which functions. Moreover it may be doubted whether improper objects can justifiably be introduced.

If these difficulties scare us off from the view that classes (including numbers) are improper objects; and if we are likewise unwilling to recognize them as proper objects, i.e. as possible arguments for any first-level function; then there is nothing for it but to regard class names as sham proper names, which would thus not really have any reference. They would have to be regarded as part of signs that had reference only as wholes

---

[B] For the distinction between first-level and second-level functions see *Function un Begriff*, pp. 26–7.

[c] 'Extension of a relation' answers to the single word '*Relation*,' which Frege uses a short for '*Umfang einer Beziehung*'—*Grundgesetze*, Vol. ii, § 162. Relations that alway hold between the same objects, like concepts under which the same objects fall, are equal in extension; and Frege holds that an extension is always an object (*Function und Begriff* pp. 18–19) although the concept or relation whose extension it is is not an object but function taking only the True or the False as its value (ibid., pp. 15, 28).

(Cf. Vol. i, § 29.) Now of course one may think it advantageous for some end to form different signs that partly resemble one another, without thereby making them into complex signs. The simplicity of a sign requires only that the parts that may be distinguished within it should have no separate reference. On this view, then, even what we usually regard as a number-sign would not really be a sign at all, but only an inseparable part of a sign. A definition of the sign '2' would be impossible; instead we should have to define many signs, which would contain '2' as an inseparable part, but could not be regarded as logically compounded of '2' and another part. It would thus be illicit to replace such an inseparable part by a letter; for as regards the content of the whole sign, there would be no complexity. The generality of arithmetical propositions would thus be lost. Again, it would be incomprehensible how we could speak of a number of classes or a number of numbers.

I think this is enough to show that this way too is barred. There is thus nothing left but to regard extensions of concepts, p. 256] or classes, as objects in the full and proper sense of the word. At the same time, however, we must admit that the interpretation we have so far put on the words 'extension of a concept' needs to be corrected.

Before we go into the matter more closely, it will be useful to track down the origin of the contradiction, by means of our symbols.[D] The supposition that $\varDelta$ is a class not belonging to itself may be expressed as follows:

⟨$\varDelta$ is the extension of some concept under which $\varDelta$ does not fall. ⟩

And the class of all classes that do not belong to themselves will be designated thus:

⟨the extension of the concept: *object that is the extension of some concept under which it does not itself fall.* ⟩

I will use the sign 'ᴠ' as short for this in the deduction that follows. . . . Accordingly I shall use

⟨'ᴠ is the extension of some concept under which ᴠ does not fall' ⟩

to express the supposition that ᴠ does not belong to itself.[E]

D These are not reproduced here. Passages in right-angled brackets ⟨ ⟩ are translated from Frege's symbolic language.

E By what is clearly a slip, Frege has 'belongs to itself.'

Now we have, by (Vb)[F]:

⟨If the concept $f(\xi)$ is equal in extension to the concept
*object that is the extension of some concept under which it does not itself
fall,*
then y falls under $f(\xi)$ if and only if y is the extension of some
concept under which y does not itself fall. ⟩

Or, using our abbreviation . . . we get[G]:

⟨If y is the extension of some concept under which y itself
does not fall, then it follows that, if y is the extension of the
concept $f(\xi)$, y falls under $f(\xi)$. ⟩   (a)

And now we get [since $f(\xi)$ may be any concept you like]:

⟨If y is the extension of some concept under which y does
not itself fall, then y falls under every concept whose extension
it is ⟩.   (β)

I.e. If y does not belong to itself, then y does belong to itself.[H]
That is one side.

On the other side we have:

⟨If y falls under every concept whose extension it is, then, if y
is the extension of the concept $f(\xi)$, y falls under $f(\xi)$. ⟩   (γ)

If we substitute for '$f(\xi)$'

⟨'ξ is the extension of some concept under which ξ does not
fall' ⟩,

we have:

⟨If y falls under every concept whose extension it is, then it
follows that, if y is the extension of the concept:
ξ *is the extension of some concept under which ξ does not fall,*
then y itself is the extension of some concept under which y
does not fall ⟩   (δ)

Taking into account our abbreviation, we get:

⟨If y falls under every concept whose extension it is, then y
is the extension of some concept under which y does not fall. ⟩ (ϵ)

I.e. If y does belong to itself, y does not belong to itself.[H] From
(ϵ) there follows

[F] Frege's Axiom (V) is deductively equivalent to the conjunction of his two theorems
(Va) and (Vb). (Va) amounts to the assertion: If two functions always have the same
value for the same argument, then they have the same value-range; in particular, if
whatever falls under either one of two concepts falls under both, then they are equal in
extension. (Vb) makes the converse assertion: If functions have the same value-range,
then they always have the same value for the same arguments; in particular, if concepts
are equal in extension then whatever falls under one falls under the other.

[G] This is a transition from 'If P, then Q if and only if R' to 'If R, then, if P, then Q.'

[H] Frege, by a slip I have corrected here, switches 'does belong' and 'does not belong.'

p. 257] ⟨ᴠ is the extension of some concept under which ᴠ
does not fall⟩   (ζ)
and from this together with (β) we get
      ⟨ᴠ falls under every concept whose extension it is.⟩   (η)
   The propositions (ζ) and (η) contradict one another. The only
place where the mistake can lie is our law (Vb), which must
therefore be false.

   . . . Along with (Vb), (V) itself has collapsed but not (Va).
There is nothing to stop our transforming an equality that holds
generally into an equality of value-ranges [in accordance with
(Va)]; all that has been shown is that the converse transformation
[in accordance with (Vb)] is not always allowable. Of course
this means admitting that the way I introduced value-ranges
(Vol. i, § 3) is not always legitimate. We cannot in general
treat the words
   'the function $\Phi(\xi)$ has the same value-range as the function
$\Psi(\xi)$'
as standing for the same thing as the words
   'the functions $\Phi(\xi)$ and $\Psi(\xi)$ always have the same value for
the same argument';
and we must take into account the possibility that there are
concepts with no extension (at any rate, none in the ordinary sense
of the word). Thus the justification of our second-level function
$\dot\epsilon\phi(\epsilon)$[1] becomes shaky. And yet such a function is indispensable
for laying the foundation of arithmetic.

   We shall now try to complete our inquiry by reaching the
falsity of (Vb) as the final result of a deduction, instead of starting
from (Vb) and thus running into a contradiction. In order to be
independent of the value-range symbol, which is always suspect,
we shall carry out the deduction quite generally, with regard to
any second-level function that takes an argument of the second
type.[j] . . .
   . . . Our complex symbol ⟨'the extension of the concept

---

[1] This symbol means 'the value-range of the function $\phi(\xi)$.' For a concept as argument,
its value will thus be the extension of that concept. On the term 'second-level function,'
see *Function und Begriff*, pp. 26–7.

[j] An argument of the second type—*Grundgesetze*, Vol. i, § 23, p. 40—is a first-
level function of one argument; i.e. a function whose single argument is always an
object, like *the square of ξ* or *the capital of ξ*. On Frege's view, a concept like ξ *is a prime
number* is a function of this sort; its value is always either the True (e.g. for the argument 3)
or the False (e.g. for 4, or the Moon, as argument). Cf. *Function und Begriff*, p. 15.

object that is the extension of some concept under which it does not fall' 〉
p. 258] will accordingly be replaced by:
〈'the M of the concept
object that is the M of some concept under which it does not fall.' 〉ᴷ
This formula contains 'M' twice over, initially and in the middle.
. . . We at once have the following result:
〈If *a* falls under every concept of which it is the M, then it
follows that, if *a* is the M of the concept
object that is the M of some concept under which it does not fall,
then *a* is itself the M of some concept under which it does not
fall. 〉
Hence:ᴸ
〈If *a* falls under every concept of which it is the M, then *a* is not
the M of the concept
object that is the M of some concept under which it does not fall. 〉   (μ)
Hence:
〈If *a* is the M of the concept
object that is the M of some concept under which it does not fall,
then *a* is the M of some concept under which *a* does not fall. 〉 (ν)
   If for short we put '$\Phi(\xi)$' instead of
〈'ξ is the M of some concept under which ξ itself does not fall' 〉,
and substitute 〈'the M of the concept $\Phi(\xi)$' 〉 for '*a*,' then we have,
by (ν),
〈The M of the concept $\Phi(\xi)$ falls under $\Phi(\xi)$ 〉
i.e. the value of our second-level function for the concept $\Phi(\xi)$ as
argument falls under this very concept. On the other hand, we
also have by (ν):
〈The M of the concept $\Phi(\xi)$ is an object that is the M of some
concept it does not fall under. 〉
I.e. There is a concept which, when taken as argument our of
second-level function, gives the same value as $\Phi(\xi)$ gives, but
under which the value in question does not fall. In other words:
For any second-level function that takes an argument of the
second type, there are two concepts yielding the same value when
taken as arguments of the function, the first of which has the

---

ᴷ The reader will probably find it helpful to think of a concrete example. He may,
e.g., take 'the M of . . .' to mean 'the number of objects falling under . . .'
   ᴸ The transition here is from 'If P, then if Q then not P' to 'If P then not Q'.

p. 259] value in question falling under it, but the second of which has not. . . .

p. 260] Our proof has been carried out without the use of propositions or symbols whose justification is in any way doubtful. Our proposition then holds good for the function $\acute{\epsilon}\phi(\epsilon)$ too, supposing this to be legitimate; it may be stated in words as follows:

If in general, for any first-level concept, we may speak of its extension, than the case arises of concepts having the same extension, although not all objects that fall under one fall under the other as well.

This, however, really abolishes the extension of the concept, p. 261] in the sense we have given the word. We may not say that in general the expression 'the extension of one concept coincides with that of another' stands for the same thing as the expression 'all objects that fall under the one concept fall under the other as well, and conversely.' We see from the result of our deduction that it is quite impossible to give the words 'the extension of the concept $\phi(\xi)$' such a sense that from concepts' being equal in extension we could always infer that every object falling under one falls under the other likewise.

Our proposition may also be reached in another way. We have:

⟨If a is not the M of any concept that a itself falls under, then, if a is the M of the concept

object that is not the M of any concept that it falls under,

it follows that a does not fall under this concept. ⟩[M]

Hence[N]:

⟨If a is not the M of any concept that it falls under, then a is not the M of the concept

object that is not the M of any concept that it falls under. ⟩ (ψ)

Hence:

⟨If a is the M of the concept

object that is not the M of any concept that it falls under,

then a falls under some concept of which it is the M. ⟩ (ω)

[M] As before, it will be easier to follow this abstract reasoning in a particular case, e.g. by taking 'the M of . . .' to mean 'the number of objects falling under . . .'

[N] This transition is one from 'If P, then, if Q, then not P' to 'If P, then not Q.'

If for short we put '$\Psi(\xi)$' instead of

⟨ 'ξ is not the M of any concept that ξ itself falls under,' ⟩

and substitute ⟨ 'the M of the concept $\Psi(\xi)$' ⟩ for 'a,' then we have, by (ω),

⟨ The M of the concept $\Psi(\xi)$ does not fall under $\Psi(\xi)$. ⟩

I.e. the value of our second-level function for the concept $\Psi(\xi)$ as argument does not fall under the concept $\Psi(\xi)$. On the other hand, we likewise have, by (ω),

⟨ The M of the concept $\Psi(\xi)$ falls under some concept of which it is the M ⟩

I.e. There is a concept which, when taken as argument of our second-level function, gives the same value as $\Psi(\xi)$ gives, and which has the value in question falling under it. Thus here likewise we have two concepts yielding the same value when taken as arguments of the second-level function, the second of which has the value in question falling under it and the first of which p. 262] has not. . . . Let us now try taking the function ⟨ *the extension of the concept $\phi(\xi)$* ⟩ as the second-level function referred to in our propositions. We then have in ⟨ the concept

object that is the extension of some concept under which it does not fall ⟩ a concept under which its own extension falls [by Proposition (ν)]; but by (ν) there is also a concept, coinciding in its extension with the one just mentioned, under which the extension in question does not fall. We should very much like to give an example. How is such a concept to be found? That is not possible without more precise specification as to our function . . . as to the extension of the concept; for our previous criterion for coincidence between concepts in their extension here leaves us in the lurch.

On the other hand, we have in ⟨ the concept

object that is not the extension of any concept that it falls under ⟩ a concept under which its own extension does not fall [by Proposition (ω)]; but by (ω) there is a concept, coinciding in extension with the one just mentioned, under which the extension in question does fall. All this discussion naturally presupposes that ' ⟨the extension of the concept $\phi(\xi)$⟩ ' is a logically correct name of a function.

In both cases we see that the exceptional case is constituted by the extension itself, in that it falls under only one of two concepts whose extension it is; and we see that the occurrence of this exception can in no way be avoided.[o] Accordingly the following suggests itself as the criterion for equality in extension: The extension of one concept coincides with that of another when every object that falls under the first concept, except the extension of the first concept, falls under the second concept likewise, and when every object that falls under the second concept, except the extension of the second concept, falls under the first concept likewise.

Obviously this cannot be taken as *defining* the extension of a concept, but only as specifying the distinctive property of this second-level function.

By transferring to value-ranges in general what we have said about extensions of concepts, we get the Axiom (V'):

⟨Two first-level functions of one argument have equal value-ranges if and only if they always have the same value for any argument that is not the value-range of either.⟩

This is to replace Axiom (V) (Vol. i, § 20, p. 36). From this law there follows (Va).[p] (Vb) on the other hand must give place to one of the laws (V'b) or (V'c) ⟨which may be stated in words as follows:

If two functions are equal in their range of values, then they have equal values for any argument that is not the value-range of one of the functions.[Ω]⟩

Let us now convince ourselves that the contradiction that arose previously between Propositions (β) and (ε) is now avoided. p. 263] We proceed just as we did in deducing (β), making use of (V'c) instead of (Vb). As before, let '⩝' be short for ⟨'the extension of the concept

object that is the extension of some concept under which it does not fall.' ⟩

o In the actual form here presented, Frege's way out of Russell's Paradox only leads to new contradictions: see the paper by W. V. Quine 'On Frege's Way Out,' *Mind*, vol. 64 (1955), pp. 145–159, and the note with the same title by P. T. Geach, *Mind*, vol. 65, pp. 408–409. The central idea, however, that the extension of the concept should itself be treated as the sole 'exceptional case,' admits of certain generalizations, which are not definitely known to regenerate paradox; the investigation of these is of considerable technical difficulty, and seems to go naturally with certain reconstructions of quantification theory. See the papers by K. J. J. Hintikka, 'Identity, variables, and impredicative definitions,' *Journal of Symbolic Logic*, vol. 21 (1956), pp. 225–245, and 'The vicious circle principle and the paradoxes,' ibid., vol. 22, pp. 245–249.

p For (Va) and (Vb) cf. footnote F on p. 168.

Ω For concepts this means: If two concepts are equal in extension, then any object that is not the extension of one of them falls under one if and only if it falls under the other.

By (V'c) we have:

⟨If the concept $f(\xi)$ is equal in extension to the concept
object that is the extension of some concept under which it does not fall,
then, if ɣ is not the extension of the latter concept, ɣ falls under
$f(\xi)$ if and only if ɣ is the extension of some concept under which
it does not fall. ⟩

Using our abbreviation we get:

⟨If the concept $f(\xi)$ is equal in extension to the concept
object that is the extension of some concept under which it does not fall,
then, if ɣ is not the same as ɣ, ɣ falls under $f(\xi)$ if and only if ɣ
is the extension of some concept under which it does not fall. ⟩

This is obvious, because of the sub-clause ⟨'if ɣ is not the same
as ɣ' ⟩, and on that very account can never lead to a contradiction. . . .

p. 265] It would here take us too far to follow out further the
result of replacing (V) by (V'). We cannot but see that many
propositions must have sub-clauses [conditions] added; but we
need scarcely fear that this will raise essential difficulties for the
course of the proofs. Anyhow, all propositions discovered up to
now will need to be checked through.

The prime problem of arithmetic may be taken to be the
problem: How do we apprehend logical objects, in particular
numbers? What justifies us in recognizing numbers as objects?
Even if this problem is not yet solved to the extent that I believed
it was when I wrote this volume, nevertheless I do not doubt
that the way to a solution has been found.